ELECTRONICS and CONTROL TECHNOLOGY using a BBC MICRO

Allan Philpot MA, MSc, Ch.Phy.

Basil Blackwell

© 1989 Alan Philpot

First published 1989

Published by Basil Blackwell Ltd
108 Cowley Road
Oxford OX4 1JF
England

British Library Cataloguing in Publication Data
Philpot, A.
  Electronics and Control Technology
  1. Electronics
  I. Title
  537.5
  ISBN 0 631 901418

Illustrated by Mike Ing and Jerry Siddall
Typeset by MULTIPLEX techniques ltd
Printed in Hong Kong
by Wing King Tong Co Ltd

Contents

Acknowledgements
I would like to thank my wife who has let me off the chores and Brian Gant for letting me use some of his circuits in this book. Allan Philpot 1989

Introduction

This book is about how electronics can be used to control mechanisms using a BBC computer.

The level of work is appropriate for GCSE. Some knowledge of electrical components, mechanisms and computers is expected. However, most of the important ideas are developed assuming no previous knowledge.

I have had difficulty in deciding whether I am writing for pupil or teacher. In the end I have made it both. As the subject is so new, I have assumed that both will need full details – especially for practical work.

The mainstream practical activities have been separately identified. These may be photocopied for use by individual pupils or groups of pupils. Where appropriate the activity sheets have a list of the equipment required for the areas to be studied, with circuit diagrams to aid the pupils. Whenever possible, I have tried to adopt a practical and problem solving approach. It is learning by doing. My difficulty is in finding the balance between saying enough to be sure that things will work and giving people freedom to develop their own ideas and solutions. Comments and/or follow-up on the activities occur throughout the book.

Three areas – computers, electronics and mechanisms

Control involves three areas, a set of instructions, electronics and mechanisms.

Sets of instructions can be written into a computer. Programs can be easily changed. This makes computers ideal for flexible, general purpose control. I have found that people readily pick up a computer language like BASIC or LOGO as they solve problems. Programs will be written in BASIC.

Electronics is also important. Electric circuits need to be linked to the computer. The best way to find out about electronics is to use it. Full practical details and theory are given.

Finally, things must move. This involves levers, gears, wheels and pulleys. This is generally called mechanisms.

Control brings these three areas together. So, each area – computers, electronics and mechanisms – is of equal importance. You may need to follow up some aspects in greater detail in other texts. I hope that this will get you started.

Equipment

Access to a BBC computer is assumed.

The principles can be applied to any computer.

There are many commercial buffer boards for linking to the BBC user ports. The emphasis here is on making your own at minimum cost and understanding the principles.

You must be prepared to put the circuits together and persevere. Everything described really does work! I suggest a basic kit of parts is:

- BBC computer
- Buffer board for linking to computer
- Various electrical components e.g. sensors, resistors, potentiometers, transistors.
- Motor reverse board
- Bits and pieces of mechanical equipment e.g. Meccano, Fischer-Technik, Technical Lego, or simply junk!

Details for DIY construction of a buffer board and motor reverse board are given in the text.

A list of suppliers' names and addresses are given in the appendix. Many of the components can be used and reused in many ways.

1 Basic Electronics

Introduction

This book assumes some previous experience of basic electronics. In order to give an idea of the starting level, we begin by reviewing the basic principles.

This chapter surveys the key ideas about electric circuits and components. It is intended to consolidate understanding and, in particular, deals with the idea of **voltage**. Voltage is generally considered to be one of the more difficult concepts in electricity. This may be so, but it is also one of the most fundamental.

The best way of understanding voltage is to gain plenty of practical experience by using a voltmeter in practical circuits. Use a voltmeter regularly to check that the voltage levels are as expected and use it to find faults when circuits do not work properly. This chapter goes on to consider the principle of the voltage (potential) divider and the transistor working as a switch.

Many of the ideas you will have met before. If this is not the case, I suggest finding an introduction from elsewhere. One thing is certain, a full understanding of the principles is best developed by first hand practical experience – so I urge the choice of a book based on a practical approach.

Activity 1.1

Questions about circuits and voltage
This is a series of true/false questions designed to test your knowledge about circuits and voltage. Discuss them in a group or answer them on your own. Either way, you should be prepared to justify your position.
Read them carefully. There are some hidden traps!
The answers to these questions can be found on page 18.

1 To set up an electric current in a circuit you need a complete circuit. True or False?

2 'Voltage difference' and 'potential difference' (pd) are different words for the same thing. Each is measured in volts. True or False?

3 Voltage difference can be thought of as the electric 'push' which drives current through part of a circuit. True or False?

4 Ordinary batteries are available with voltages in multiples of 1.5 V. This voltage is sometimes called the emf (electromotive force). True or False?

5 A fresh battery can supply a wide variation of current – from almost zero to 1 amp or so. Its voltage, however, does not change much. True or False?

Activity 1.1 continued

6 Current is the amount of charge passing each second. Current in a connecting wire is carried by electrons moving. True or False?

7 Ohm's law states that the size of the current (I) flowing through a component will be proportional to the pd (V) between its ends i.e. V = IR. True or False?

8 Ohm's law applies to resistors and most other components. True or False?

9 The resistance of a component shows how difficult it is to 'push' current through it. The unit resistance is measured in is the Ohm. True or False?

10 A bulb carries a current of 0.3 A when a pd of 6 V is applied across it. The resistance is 2 Ohms. True or False?

Circuit components

There are many different circuit components (e.g. lamp, diode, resistor). These behave in different ways when a voltage difference (potential difference) is applied between their ends. For example, a lamp will get brighter as the voltage difference is increased. However, the current through a diode depends on the way round it is connected, as well as the applied voltage difference. Some components respond to other changes e.g.:
the resistance of a thermistor depends on temperature and
the resistance of an ldr (light dependent resistor) depends on light level.

Activity 1.2

This checks whether you understand the behaviour of some common components and if you know their circuit symbols.
There are six circuit components. Each has four cards.
Sort out which of the 24 cards links with each component.
It's easiest to do this by photocopying pages 2 and 3 then cutting them into pieces. It's better when you discuss your answers with someone else.

1 the resistance falls as it gets hotter	2 symbol easy flow	9 used when you need easy current flow in one direction but very little current in the opposite direction	10 symbol -t°
3 looks like:– mark on body same as on symbol	4 can only carry very current (usually has a resistor – around 500R, in series to keep current low)	11 symbol 	12 gives out light and some heat
5 gives out light but always remains cold	6 symbol 	13 resistance falls as the light falling on it gets brighter. (often used as a light sensor)	14 symbol
7 looks like:– 	8 allows more current to flow as its temperature is raised	15 looks like:– or	16 has a small resistance in one direction and a large resistance in the other

17 allows more current to flow as the light falling on it is increased.	18 looks like:– 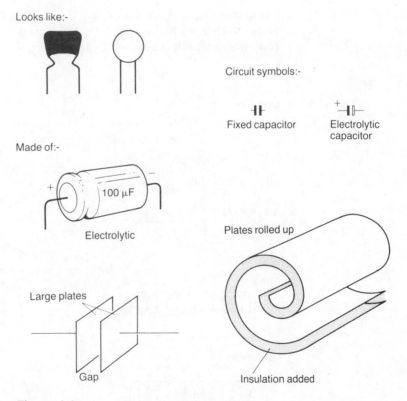	diode	lamp [or bulb]
19 looks like:–	20 resistance increases as it gets hot	light emitting diode [led]	light dependent resistor [ldr]
21 the greater the voltage difference (applied to its ends), the greater the current flowing through it. (i.e. Ohm's law V = IR)	22 symbol	thermistor	resistor

23 looks like:–	24 a colour code is widely used to show how well it restricts current flow.	Basic electronic components
		Card sort
		    Cut into sections
		    Can you arrange them into 6 groups?	

Capacitors (fig 1.1) are widely used in electronics, and are certain to have been included in an introductory course.

Looks like:-

Circuit symbols:-

Fixed capacitor   Electrolytic capacitor

Made of:-

Electrolytic

Plates rolled up

Large plates

Gap

Insulation added

Figure 1.1

Activity 1.3

This is intended to test your knowledge about capacitors.
Photocopy this page and see if you can fill in the missing words in the series of statements about capacitors.

A **capacitor** stores electric (1) _____ when a potential difference (voltage difference) is applied between its ends. Charge is released when the applied (2) _____ is reduced.

Capacitors are made from two large plates electrically (3) _____ from each other. When a pd is applied, charge flows onto one plate and off the other. The capacitance is the amount of charge which can be stored under an electrical 'pressure' difference of (4) ___ ____. The unit used to measure capacitance is the (5) _____.

You might expect the capacitance to become larger as the plates are made (6) _____. Indeed, this is so. In practice, large plates are 'rolled up' to reduce them to a reasonable size. They become like miniature toilet rolls with electrically insulated double sheets!

The capacitance also depends on the (7) ___ between the plates and the kind of insulator used to separate them. You will come across 'electrolytic' capacitors. These are high value capacitors which use special materials between the plates. They must be connected the right way round.

Capacitors are used to (8) _____ out voltage fluctuations and to control the length of pulse in timer circuits.

The missing words can be found on page 20.

Inductors (fig 1.2) are less common than capacitors. The inductive effect is associated with the magnetic field of an electrical current. Relays use this magnetic effect and act as inductors.

Looks like:-

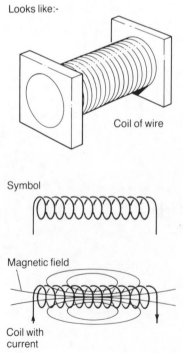

Coil of wire

Symbol

Magnetic field

Coil with
current

Figure 1.2

Activity 1.4

This is another exercise where you have to fill in the missing words. It will test your knowledge of the key facts about inductors. Use a photocopy of this page to write in your answers.

Inductors depend on the magnetic field of an electric current. They are made from a coil of wire which stores (1) _____ in its magnetic field when a current flows. The magnetic effect is increased with a (2) _____ number of turns in the coil of wire and with the introduction of a (3) _____ _____ core.

The magnetic field gives rise to 'electro-magnetic induction' effects. Circuits seem to dislike changes in the magnetic field linked with them. When changes happen, potential differences are 'induced' in an attempt to maintain the original (4) _____ _____. This is called the induced (5) ___.

It's similar to us when asked to do the washing up while sitting in front of the TV – we also resist change! The magnetic effect of an electric current is used in motors and relay switches. It's also used in transformers. So, all these components will have an inductive effect.

The inductive effect in a circuit tends to (6) ____ up changes in current.

There is a very important practical point. When you switch off components which have a magnetic field, the stored energy can drive a current back through the circuit. The effect is called the 'back emf' and can be of quite high voltage. You usually use a (7) _____ to provide a path for the (8) _____ current. If you do not, you may get sparking at switches or destroy circuit components.

The missing words can be found on page 20.

Practical ways of setting up circuits

Circuit diagrams

In practice circuits are usually built up from a circuit diagram. The symbols used for a number of simple components have been included in Activity 1.2.

In circuit diagrams the positive (+ve) voltage supply is drawn as a horizontal line (or rail) at the top and the negative (−ve) at the bottom (fig 1.3). The negative is usually made the reference level. This is considered to be at zero voltage and is called the '**earth**' or '**ground**'.

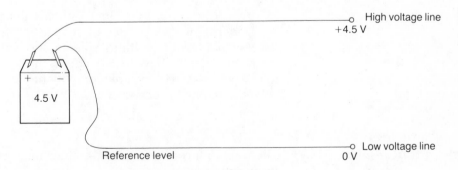

Figure 1.3

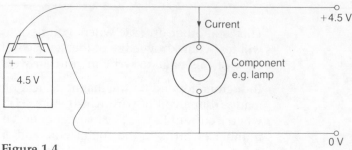

Figure 1.4

When components are connected between the two lines charge will flow, resulting in a current (fig 1.4). Conventionally electric current is considered to flow from +ve to −ve. However electrons which usually make up this current, flow the other way. This can give rise to confusion. Some people talk about electron current . In this book we will always refer to the conventional current. This flows from +ve to −ve.

It is an advantage to be able to lay out the components in the same order as in the circuit diagram – especially for beginners. This will enable you to check whether you have all the components you need and that they are in the correct order for the circuit to work properly.

Connecting components together

There are many methods for building up circuits from components. Each has advantages and disadvantages.

In all cases, it's essential to make **'good' connections**. This will avoid much frustration in trying to work out why a circuit won't work! 'Good' connections have a very small contact resistance and are reliable. Contact should not be broken when the circuit is moved! Clearly, a quick way of making connections has much to recommend it. However, a piece of twisted wire or an unreliable 'croc' clip connection will lead to considerable frustration in complex circuits.

Plug and socket systems tend to be expensive. There are many of these on the market but they are of different sizes and are not compatible. I have found that a 4 mm barrel terminal block (RS 423–554)* (fig 1.5) makes a very convenient socket. Armed with a screwdriver, all kinds of plug and even bare wires can be connected into it. The barrel terminal block will be recommended as a connecting system in the DIY circuits described later in the book. **Please be advised. Take time and trouble to make 'good' connections**.

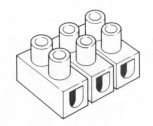

Figure 1.5

'To solder or not to solder?' – that is the question.

Soldering makes reliable permanent or semi-permanent connections. It's easy to do, but takes time. Solder is also surprisingly expensive. Clearly it's inconvenient to have to de-solder components for re-use. Broadly speaking, when you need to link components into a semi-permanent system, soldering is the best answer.

Some examples of connecting systems

There are four commonly used connecting systems for building up circuits from components.

*RS numbers refer to the relevant number in the RS components catalogue – for further details see Appendix page 197.

Baseboard – components are laid out as shown in a circuit diagram and fixed onto a baseboard.

Breadboard – components are poked into holes to link into a network of standard connections.

Stripboard – components are soldered into strips of copper connections through a matrix of holes.

Printed circuit board – (pcb) – components are soldered into a network of specially designed circuit connections.

These are discussed in more detail in the next sections.

Baseboards

Baseboards have a particular advantage. They allow you to set out the circuit components in the positions shown in the circuit diagram. Therefore they are most suitable for the early stages of electronics. On the softboard and matrix board bases described below soldering is used to make connections. Wires with 'croc' clip connectors at each end make a useful alternative for temporary connections. There are other systems available which use springs or screws instead of solder.

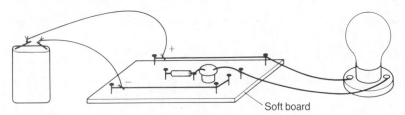

Soft board

Figure 1.6

(1a) Softboard base (fig 1.6)

This uses a piece of softboard (25 cm × 20 cm approx) and copper-plated nails as posts for soldering components on to. Connection wires are made from uninsulated nickel-plated copper wire. Components have to be soldered into place and this can be time consuming.

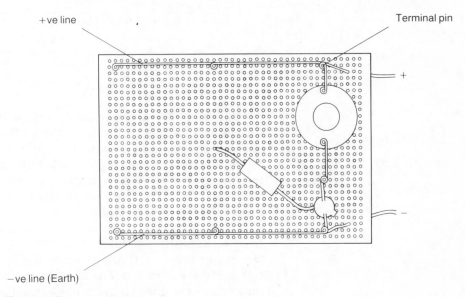

+ve line   Terminal pin

−ve line (Earth)

Figure 1.7

(1b) Matrix board base (fig 1.7)

The matrix board is a panel (15 cm × 11 cm) drilled with holes on a 0.25 cm grid (RS 433–295). Terminal pins (RS 433–624) are inserted into the holes and provide posts to which the components are soldered.

Solderless breadboard

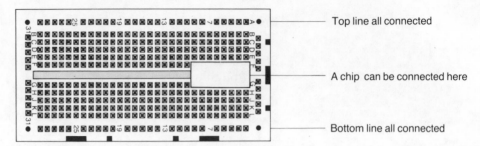

Figure 1.8

This is a very convenient way of making temporary connections. The 'breadboard' has a pattern of holes (fig 1.8) some of which are linked together underneath the board (fig 1.9). Components are simply poked into the holes. In this way connections are made between them. Chips can be fitted across the central channel. The system is known by other names such as prototype-board or Veroboard.

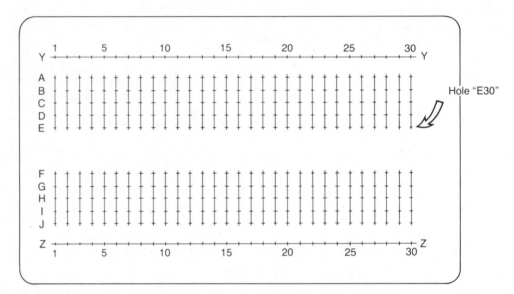

Figure 1.9

But, take care! Components plugged into the holes MUST be free of insulation and solder, otherwise, the sockets will be damaged. So a special batch of unsoldered components should be kept for use with breadboards. Single-strand wire is needed to make the connections. The upper limit for the diameter of the wire is about 0.85 mm. You will find it useful to keep short lengths of insulated single-strand wire with bared ends for making links between the sets of holes.

Note that there are letters and numbers on the block which can be used to identify particular holes (fig 1.9). This is helpful in discussing circuit construction. There are some disadvantages to the system. You have to modify the circuit layout to fit the pattern of the holes. The holes are quite close together so good eyesight and deft fingers are needed. The main advantages are the fast speed of construction and the convenient re-use of components.

Stripboard

Stripboard is widely used for making permanent soldered connections. It has a matrix of holes connected by parallel strips of copper (fig 1.10). The 0.25 cm pitch (0.1″ of olden days) has the same spacing as the legs on chips (RS 433–826), So they can be connected into the system easily. Stripboard with a larger separation of holes is also available. Components are pushed through the holes from the blank face and soldered into place. The circuit layout has to be adapted to fit the strips of copper. (This is shown in fig 1.11.)

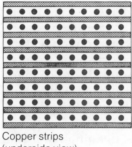

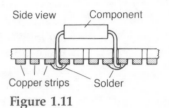

Side view   Component

Copper strips   Solder

Figure 1.11

Copper strips
(underside view)

Figure 1.10

You may need to make breaks in some of the copper strips. These are usually shown by an 'x' in circuit layout diagrams. Breaks can be made using a small drill bit or special tool (e.g. RS 543–535).

Printed circuit board (pcb)

This is another way for making permanent connections. A pcb is specially designed and constructed for a particular circuit. It has a map of thin conducting strips on the underside of the board (fig 1.12). Small holes drilled in the board allow components to be pushed through from the blank face and soldered into place. Thus, a permanent complete circuit can be constructed.

Ready made pcb's can be purchased for particular circuits, but it is possible to make your own. To do this, start with a board which has one side uniformly covered in a thin film of copper. Etch away the unwanted copper using ferric chloride solution.

Circuits are usually designed from the component or 'top' side view. If you etch the top view of your circuit onto the board it will be the 'wrong' way round. The top view needs to be inverted. Take great care! This has floored more people than you would expect!

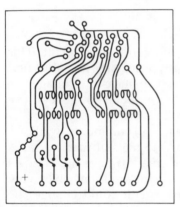

Figure 1.12

Mark out your circuit on the copper layer using a special felt pen which is not water soluble. This makes a barrier between the copper and the etching chemical. The remaining metal can be etched away by placing the board in a ferric chloride solution. Ferric chloride is nasty, corrosive stuff and must be handled with great care. At some stage, before or after etching, holes are drilled in the board to accept components. Finally these are soldered into place. Full details of how to make a pcb are given on page 101, where one is used for a relay motor reverse board.

In practice, pcb's would only be produced commercially when a circuit needs to be built in a large quantity. Fortunately, this is true for the BBC user port interface which we will build later. Industrial pcb's are now designed with components soldered directly onto the conducting face. This is known as 'surface mounting' of components. It saves a lot of hassle in drilling holes, reduces costs and saves time.

We will use breadboard for temporary circuits and stripboard or pcb for permanent circuits.

The importance of voltage

A voltage difference is needed to drive a current through a component. The word **potential** can be used instead of voltage – it means the same thing. The simplest method for providing a voltage is a battery. For a single component in a circuit the general relationship between voltage and current is:

the greater the voltage difference, the greater the current. However, the current can be affected by factors other than the voltage. For example, for a thermistor it also depends on temperature; for a light-dependent resistor (ldr) it also depends on light level; and for a transistor (collector to emitter current) it depends mainly on the base voltage. This will be explained in more detail later (see page 17). If too many factors become involved the situation could rapidly get out of hand. However, in practice devices are usually built to respond to only one or two factors. For example, resistors are usually insensitive to changes in temperature.

Voltage difference is linked with energy changes. For example, when a current flows through a resistor, electrical energy is converted into heat. The energy released each second depends on the voltage difference and the current. The formal definition of a volt is based on this principle. The voltage difference can be regarded as the 'push' or 'pressure difference' which drives current through a component.

Measuring voltage difference

We need to be able to measure the voltage difference in a circuit. This helps to show how the circuit is working. It is particularly useful to find faults when it isn't working. Instruments used to measure voltage are called voltmeters. There are two main types of voltmeters in general use – the moving coil voltmeter and the digital voltmeter (fig 1.13).

The moving coil voltmeter is relatively cheap and commonly available. It needs a small current (typically about 15 mA) to make it work. It takes this from the circuit. Often this current is too small to have much effect on the circuit. However, when currents in a circuit are themselves very small, adding a moving coil voltmeter to the circuit could change the conditions and give 'false' readings.

A digital voltmeter effectively draws no current from the circuit and acts as a 'perfect' voltmeter. It could be used if you wanted to measure the voltage actually present. A digital voltmeter tends, however, to be rather expensive and uses an internal battery. Unfortunately, batteries run down.

A cathode ray oscilloscope (CRO) also acts as a perfect voltmeter drawing no current from the circuit. It is cumbersome to use but something to try if you want a challenge. CROs are used to display rapidly changing voltage levels.

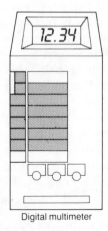

Digital multimeter

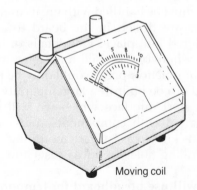

Moving coil

Figure 1.13

Electronic control

There are perhaps two principal ideas used in electronic control. One is the use of a voltage (potential) divider and the other is the use of a transistor as a switch. Both of these ideas will be discussed in this chapter.

The voltage (potential) divider

We have seen that in electronic circuit diagrams that the voltage difference given by the supply is shown as positive (high voltage) and low voltage (or earth) **rails**, as shown in fig 1.14. You can think of these rails as lines coming from a voltage supply, such as a battery (cell), or the low voltage mains supply. In fig 1.14 the voltage difference from the supply is 5 V.

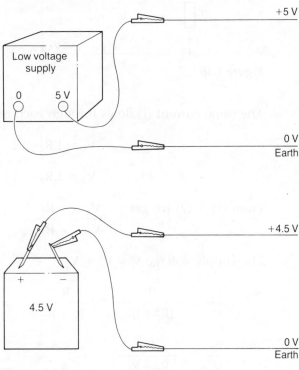

Figure 1.14

However, we may not want to use a 5 V voltage difference. We may wish to use a component which needs a much smaller voltage difference, say 1 V. To enable us to use this component the 5 V supply can be divided into smaller voltages by using resistors in series. For example, in fig 1.15 the voltage difference is divided into a 4 V difference and a 1 V difference.

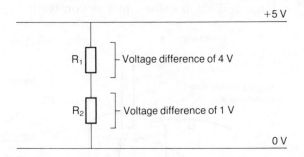

Figure 1.15

This was done by adding two resistors in series. In this case resistor R_1 must have the larger resistance. More of the available voltage difference will then be required to drive the current through resistor R_1 than through resistor R_2.

Question

If you divide up a voltage in this way, do the voltage differences through the various resistors always add up to the voltage difference of the supply?

This can be treated mathematically using the formula V = IR (fig 1.16).

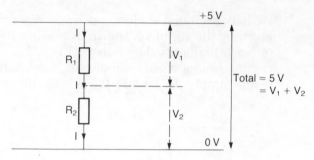

Figure 1.16

The same current (I) flows through each resistor, so, for each resistor

$$V_1 = I.R_1 \quad \ldots (1)$$

$$V_2 = I.R_2 \quad \ldots (2)$$

From (1) ÷ (2) we get

$$\frac{V_1}{V_2} = \frac{R_1}{R_2}$$

The supply voltage $V = V_1 + V_2$

So,

$$\frac{V_1}{V} = \frac{IR_1}{IR_1 + IR_2} = \frac{R_1}{R_1 + R_2}$$

and

$$\frac{V_2}{V} = \frac{R_2}{R_1 + R_2}$$

By using different value resistors, it is possible to get any voltage you wish between 0 and the supply level. In practice this is made easy by using a variable resistor sometimes called a rheostat, potentiometer or 'pot' (fig 1.17). It can be made from a coil of wire wound into a circle (ends D and E). A sliding connector (S) can be turned, to make contact at any point along the wire. In this way the total voltage can be divided into large and small values, just as you want.

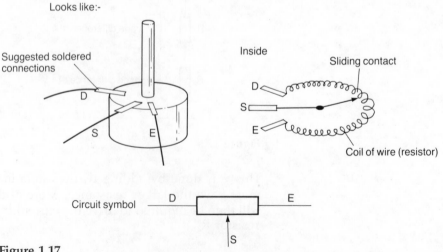

Figure 1.17

Activity 1.5

THE VOLTAGE DIVIDER

The voltage divider (also called a potential divider) is one of the most important ideas in electronics. It is used when you want to get a particular voltage level by dividing the supply voltage difference into two parts.

The aim is to see how the voltage divider works in practice and to give experience in using a voltmeter.

You need:
- low voltage supply (4.5 V battery or 5 V power unit)
- resistors (2 × 1 K and 1 × 10 K)
- voltmeter (0 to 6 V)
- variable resistor (potentiometer) 10 K max
- breadboard
- single-strand connecting wires
- 'croc' clip connectors
- soldering iron (optional)

1 Connect two 1 K resistors in series across the power supply rails (figs 1.18 and 1.19).

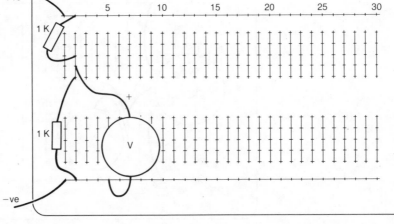

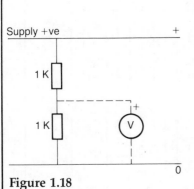

Figure 1.18

Figure 1.19

Use the voltmeter to measure the voltage difference (potential difference) across both resistors and then across each one in turn. Make sure that the +ve terminal is always connected to the higher voltage (or potential).

The supply voltage is divided between the two resistors. Does each have half of this potential difference?

2 Connect the 10 K resistor in series with a 1 K as shown in fig 1.20. Measure the voltage (potential) difference across each resistor as before.

Does the 10 K resistor have ten times the voltage difference of the 1 K resistor? Is the sum of the voltage differences equal to the voltage difference from the supply?

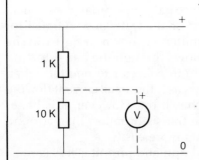

Figure 1.20

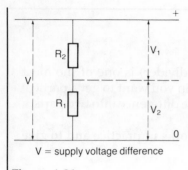

V = supply voltage difference

Figure 1.21

3 In general, for any two resistors R_1 and R_2 in series (fig 1.21).

$$V = V_1 + V_2$$

$$V_1 = \left[\frac{R_1}{R_1 + R_2} \right] . V$$

$$V_2 = \left[\frac{R_2}{R_1 + R_2} \right] . V$$

Do these relations work for your investigations?

4 By using different value resistors, you can get any voltage difference you wish between 0 and the supply level. Connect the variable resistor as shown in fig 1.22. You will need to find a way of connecting the ends to the breadboard. Soldering short lengths of single-strand wire is recommended. Check the voltage reading at S as the setting is changed. Now you can obtain any voltage level between 0 V and the supply level.
Keep this circuit set up for the transistor investigation, Activity 1.7.

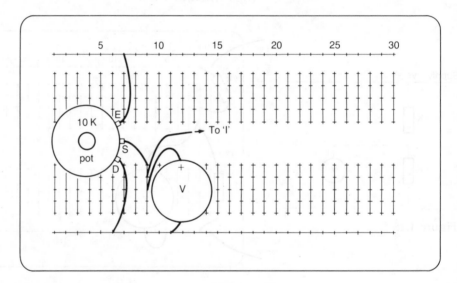

Figure 1.22

The transistor as a current controller

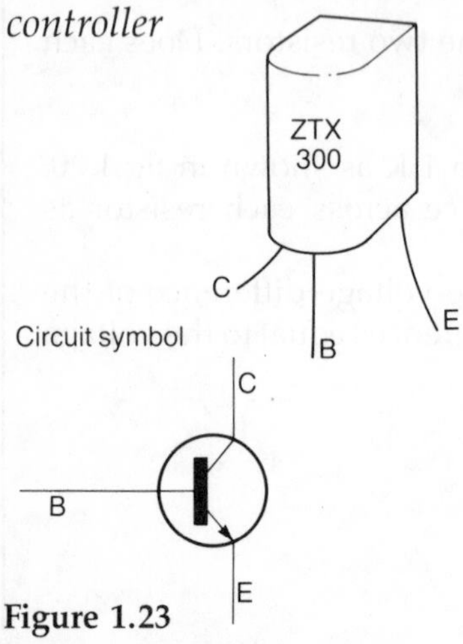

ZTX 300

Circuit symbol

Figure 1.23

The second key idea in electronics is how a transistor can be used as a switch. (The first key idea is how to obtain a reduced voltage using a voltage divider.) Instead of working a switch by hand, a transistor switch is controlled by voltage levels. Transistors act as a kind of gate which controls the current. They are similar to sluice gates in a canal where small changes in the gate setting have a large effect on the water flow. A transistor has three legs – the base, collector and emitter as shown in fig 1.23. The current which is **collected** at the collector flows through the transistor and is **emitted** at the emitter. It flows easily, from collector to emitter, when the base is connected to high voltage. In this case, the small current flowing into the transistor through the base switches it on. However, it is better to think about voltage level controlling the transistor rather than current. This helps you understand complex circuits more easily.

There are two kinds of transistor, called **npn** and **pnp**. It is less confusing to keep to one type. We will concentrate on the 'npn'.

To sum up, a transistor acts as an electronic switch (fig 1.24). Instead of turning the switch on and off by hand the current is controlled by a change in the base voltage level. (Base voltage above a critical level = on, Base voltage below this level = off.)

Activity 1.6 investigates the use of a transistor as a current controller. In Activity 1.7 the critical voltage needed to switch a transistor is investigated.

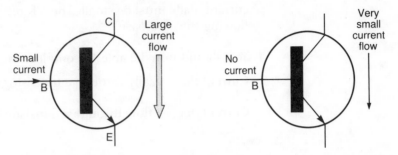

Figure 1.24

Activity 1.6

The aim here is to see how to use a transistor as a switch.

You need:
- low voltage dc supply (4.5 V battery or 5 V power unit)
- transistor e.g. BC108 or ZTX300
- 6 V, (0.06 A) lamp in holder*
- 1 K resistor
- breadboard (or alternative)
- connections

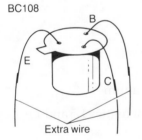

BC108

Extra wire

Figure 1.25

The details which follow apply to breadboard. (There are many other ways of making up the circuits. Use whichever you have to hand.)

1 If you have kept the circuit used in Activity 1.5, add your components to the breadboard.
   If using a breadboard solder short lengths of single strand wire onto the transistor legs to make easy connection to the board – fig 1.25.
   (*In soldering, it's good practice to use a 'heat sink' to stop the transistor getting too hot. Do this by holding the leg close to the case with a pair of pliers or a croc clip. These conduct heat away from the transistor – fig 1.26.*)
   Connect up the circuit shown in fig 1.27.

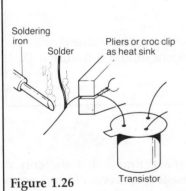

Soldering iron
Solder
Pliers or croc clip as heat sink

Transistor

Figure 1.26

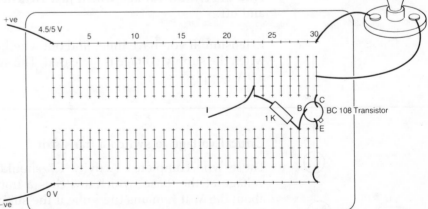

Figure 1.27

*Take care that you really do have this lamp. It won't work otherwise. An led with a 300 R resistor in series is an alternative.

2 Connect (I) (linked to the base) to high voltage (the +ve rail) Does the lamp light?

3 Connect (I) to low voltage (earth).
Does the lamp light?
In your circuit, current passes through the lamp into the transistor (at the collector) and out at the emitter. A small base current turns the transistor on – letting it pass a large current. Note that the base current really must be small. The 1 K resistor stops any large current flowing into the base.

4 You should now be able to complete the sentences:–

Current flows easily through a transistor (collector to emitter) when
. . . .

Current doesn't flow through a transistor (collector to emitter) when
. . . .

Keep the transistor connected for later use.

Activity 1.7

What is the critical voltage to switch a transistor?
What electrical voltage level is needed at the base to switch the transistor on/off?

You need:
- low voltage dc supply (4.5 V battery or 5 V power unit)
- 9 V dc supply (optional)
- 6 V (0.6 A) lamp in holder
- transistor BC108 or ZTX300
- 1 K resistor
- breadboard
- connections
- voltmeter (0–6 V)
- variable resistor (potentiometer) 10 K maximum

Set up your circuit in the same way as you did in Activities 1.5 and 1.6.

You need to get different voltage levels at the base of our transistor. This is done conveniently by using a voltage (or potential) divider.

Find the critical voltage which just switches the transistor between on and off.

Extension: If you have time, find out whether the critical value changes when the supply voltage is increased. The system should still work with a 9 V supply.

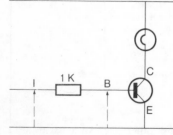

Figure 1.28

Critical voltage to switch a transistor

Those who completed Activity 1.7 should have found that the critical voltage at the 'base' which switches a transistor between off and on is about 0.6 V. It remains the same if the supply voltage is increased. There is one small problem. You may have noticed that you did not measure the voltage at the base itself. It was measured at the point I which is separated from the base by a 1 K resistor (fig 1.28).

Now remember that the 1 K resistor is used to make sure that very little current flows into the base. (Transistors are designed for this. If a large current flows into the base they get hot and do not work properly.) Since the current passing throught the 1 K resistor is very small then only small voltage difference is needed to drive it through. So, we hope that the voltage at I is much the same as at the base of the transistor. It is worth noting that there are two kinds of transistor. The ones recommended here are 'npn' transistors. The other kind, known as 'pnp' transistors are connected in a different way. They switch on when the base is connected to low voltage and switch off when the base voltage is high (fig 1.29). With one exception, we will always use the npn kind.

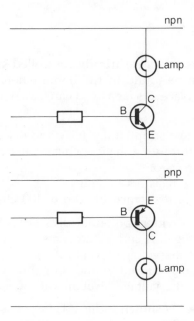

Figure 1.29

Summary

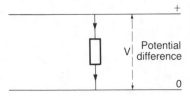

Figure 1.30

Voltage difference (or potential difference) indicates the 'push' driving current through a component. The current geneally increases if the voltage difference increases fig 1.30.

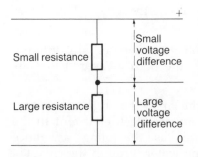

Figure 1.31

Voltage divider (or potential divider) When a voltage difference is applied across two components in series the voltage difference is divided between the two components. The larger resistance has the larger voltage difference across it. This is an important way of getting a required voltage level fig 1.31.

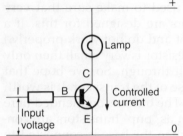

Figure 1.32

A transistor can act as a switch. A base voltage greater than 0.6 V causes a large current to flow between collector and emitter (for npn type transistor). The base must never carry a large current and a resistor is used to limit base current. fig 1.32.

It is essential to have a system which will give **good, reliable electrical connections**. There are many types of system. Breadboard is particularly useful for temporary connections and stripboard for permanent ones.

Consolidation questions

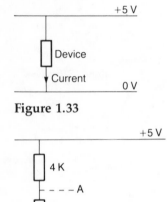

Figure 1.33

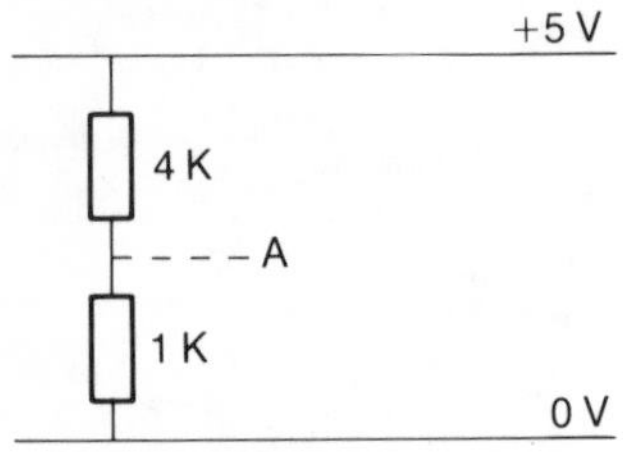

Figure 1.34

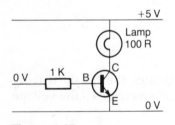

Figure 1.35

1 Transistors act as electrically controlled switches. Name some devices which can be found in the home where 'electronic' switching could be taking place. As far as you can, say what controlling action is taking place.

2 You have two supply rails +5 V and 0 V (fig 1.33). How much current will flow through a device which consists of the following?
   a a 10 K resistor
   b two 10 K resistors in series
   c a lamp of resistance 100 R (i.e. 100 Ohms)

3 A voltage divider (potential divider) is made up from two resistors shown in fig 1.34 connected across a 5 V supply.
   a What is the voltage level at A?
   b How much current would flow through each resistor?
   c What is the voltage level at A if the supply is made 10 V?

4 A transistor is shown in fig 1.35. The base is at 0 V. Will the transistor be on or off?
   The current flowing through the bulb (resistance 100 R) was found to be 1 μA (μ A = microamp) = 10^{-6}A
   What is the approximate voltage level at C?
   Estimate the resistance of the transistor (collector–emitter).

Solutions

Activity 1.1

(1) **Only half true**. You also need a battery or energy supply. This drives the electric charge through the components.

(2) **True**. Potential difference (pd) and voltage difference are different words for *exactly* the same thing. They are both measured in volts using a voltmeter.

(3) **True**, if you wish. Generally speaking, the larger the pd (V), the larger the current (I). Some people like to compare electric current to the flow of water in a plumbing circuit. In this case the voltage difference is similar to a pressure difference driving water through the circuit.

(4) **True** as long as you appreciate that the *voltage* is really the voltage difference developed between the terminals of the battery.

If you follow this through in detail, the emf is the maximum available pd to drive current round a circuit. When a battery is used, some of this pd is needed to drive the current inside the battery. (The term emf goes back to the early days of electricity. 'Force' is now measured in newtons. This means the electromotive force measured in volts is no longer a comfortable term. Perhaps we should invent a new term referring to the energy supplied by a battery.)

(5) **True in theory**! In practice, the voltage supplied by the battery to the outside circuit will fall when higher currents are drawn. This is because some of the pd is required to drive the current inside the battery.

Low voltage power supply units working from the mains usually give a steady voltage no matter what reasonable current is drawn.

(6) **True**. 60 000 000 000 000 000 000 electrons (6×10^{18}), a very large number! – passing each second is one AMP of current. The electrons move in the opposite direction to the 'conventional' current.

(7) **True**, but you need to take care about the nature of the component. It originally applied to a metal wire kept at constant temperature. It works for resistors.

(8) **Only partly true**. Ohm's law works for resistors and metal wire kept at a constant temperature. It doesn't work for most other components, e.g. metal filament lamps, diodes and transistors. These have different relationships between the current and the applied pd.

(9) **True**. Resistance is measured by the pd needed to push 1 amp through it. If a component has a large resistance, you need a large voltage difference to drive 1 amp through. In practice, many components cannot carry as much as 1 amp, so you would have to *estimate* the pd which would be required for 1 amp. Your calculation would be based on small current measurements.

(10) **False**. 0.3 A needs a pd of 6 V.

0.1 A need a pd of 6/3 = 2 V.

1A needs a pd of 2 × 10 = 20V. The pd needed to drive 1 amp through is 20 V, so the resistance is 20 Ohms. Note that a current of 1 amp would 'blow' the bulb!

You could also use the formula 'V = IR', which should give the same result.

Activity 1.2

The intended groupings are:

	card numbers
resistor	19, 21, 22, 24
lamp	7, 12, 14, 20
diode	2, 3, 9, 16
thermistor	1, 8, 10, 15
ldr (light-dependent resistor)	11, 13, 17, 23
led (light-emitting diode)	4, 5, 6, 18*

*The led is a diode and card 16 would also apply here.

Activity 1.3

The intended answers are:

1 energy
2 larger
3 soft iron
4 magnetic field
5 emf
6 slow
7 diode
8 induced

Activity 1.4

The missing words are:

1 charge or energy
2 voltage or potential
3 insulated
4 one volt
5 Farad
6 larger
7 gap or distance
8 smooth or even out

Consolidation questions

1 Examples will include any device where a changing voltage level causes a switching action in a circuit, e.g. electronic timers – radio alarm, video timer, central heating timer
infra-red sensors – TV controllers, movement sensors, burglar alarms
light sensors – automatic switching on a light at night
temperature sensors – heating, fire alarms.
2 0.5 mA, 0.25 mA, 0.05 A or 50 mA
3 1 V, 1 mA, 2 V
4 off, approx 5 V, 5000 K or 5 M

2 The transistor as part of a control system

Introduction

In the previous chapter we saw that a transistor can be used to switch a lamp on and off. This chapter looks at how a transistor can be built into a larger control system. Our approach will concentrate on the voltage levels involved. We will see how to make the system sensitive to changes in light and temperature and extend it to control a relay – a mechanical switch.

The systems approach

A **systems approach** means concentrating on what a **system** does. There is an 'input' which produces some kind of **output**. Usually you do not have to be concerned about how the system works – just how it behaves. This approach can be used for many systems not just electrical ones (fig 2.1).

Figure 2.1

In electronic systems, you usually look at the input and output voltage levels (fig 2.2). Then the overall effect can be sorted out without getting too bogged down in detail. It is a very powerful way of looking at what happens in a circuit – especially when they become complex.

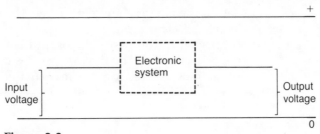

Figure 2.2

The systems approach is particularly useful for integrated circuits, often called **chips** or simply **ICs**. An integrated circuit has many **components** like transistors, capacitors and resistors linked together on a single silicon base. It is made by diffusing impurities into the base and is far too complex to make yourself! With a systems approach, however, you don't need to worry about what's inside. It is easier to on work out what is happening in a circuit by considering voltage levels rather than currents. This is why we placed great emphasis voltage measurement in Chapter 1. It is also easy to measure voltage levels using a voltmeter without having to break into the circuit and disrupt its performance.

*Transistors as voltage
inverters*

The transistor will be treated as a system. You can set up a voltage level at the input to the transistor and see how it affects voltage at the output side of the transistor. This is done in Activity 2.1. The main problem is identifying the place where the output voltage is found.

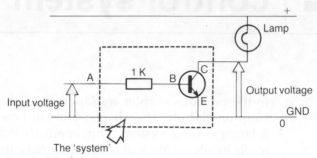

Figure 2.3

The **input** is the voltage applied at the base (fig 2.3). (In practice it is applied to the resistor connected to the base.) The output is the voltage which appears at the collector. The lamp is needed to complete the circuit. Consider it as the **load** which is controlled by the transistor.

At this stage, you should try Activity 2.1.

Activity 2.1

The transistor as a voltage inverter

The aim of this activity is to see how the transistor acts as a 'system'.

Set up a voltage level as the input to the transistor and see how it affects voltage at the **output** side of the transistor. In other words, treat the transistor as a **system** and examine the input and output voltages of the system.

You need:
- 5 V dc supply (battery or low voltage supply)
- transistor BC108 or ZTX300
- 1 K resistor
- 6 V (0.06 A) lamp in holder
- 10 K potentiometer ('pot')
- breadboard and connecting wires
- voltmeter (0–5 V)

1 Set up the circuit shown in fig 2.4. The breadboard layout is shown in fig 2.5. The input is the voltage applied at (A) to the resistor connected to the base. The output is the voltage which appears at the collector (C). The device which is controlled by the transistor is sometimes referred to as the **load**. In this case the lamp is the load.

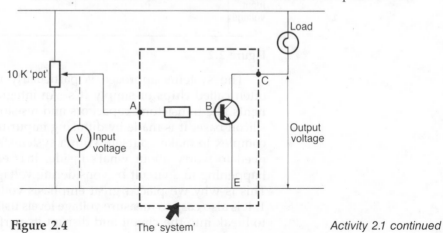

Figure 2.4   The 'system'   *Activity 2.1 continued*

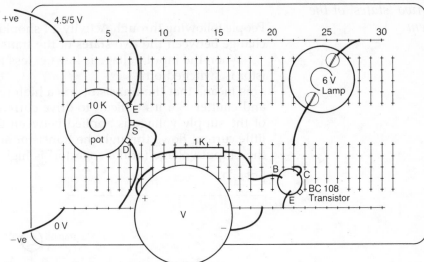

Figure 2.5

2 Adjust the 'pot' (potentiometer) to give the maximum input voltage. Measure this with the voltmeter.

3 Move the voltmeter connection to measure the output voltage (at the collector). You only need to change the positive connection. The negative should remain connected to the ground/earth of your circuit.
   What is your reading? (The lamp should be on).

4 Now find out what happens as you reduce the input voltage from high voltage down to 0 V. Pay special attention to what happens between 1 and 0 V.
   Record your findings in a table like that shown in fig 2.6.

Input voltage	Output voltage	Lamp ON/OFF
Volts	Volts	
5		ON
4		
3		
2		
1		
0.5		
0		

— Transistor also said to be on or off

Figure 2.6

5 When the lamp is on we often say that the transistor is switched on. This means that there is a low resistance between collector (C) and emitter (E). It's easy to drive current through the transistor and very little voltage difference is required to do so. So, if you measure a small voltage at the collector – less than 0.5 V – most of the voltage difference of the supply is available to drive current through the lamp. You can simpilfy the voltage levels to two states – low and high.

6 Can you complete the sentences?
   When the transistor input voltage is low the output voltage is . . .
   When the transistor input voltage is high the output voltage is . . .

*The two 'states' of the
system*

People following through Activity 2.1 should find that there is a fairly rapid change between the two **states** of the transistor – on and off.

When the input voltage is low i.e. less than 0.5 V (approx.), the transistor is switched off.

This means that the transistor has a high resistance between the collector and emitter. So, it's difficult to drive current through. Even though most of the supply voltage is applied between the collector and emitter, very little current flows through the transistor and the lamp is off. In this case the output voltage (at the collector) is high (fig 2.7).

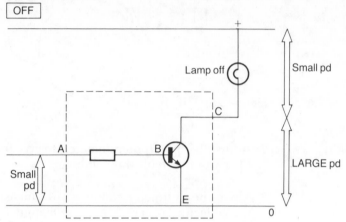

Figure 2.7

When the input voltage is made high the transistor is switched on. In this case, the resistance between the collector and emitter becomes small. This leads to a low voltage output at C. This gives a large voltage difference to drive current through the load, so the lamp is on.

The relation between input and output voltages of the system is usually stated as

    high/low : low/high.

In other words:

- when the input voltage (pd) is high (greater than 0.7 V) the output voltage at the collector is low (fig 2.8).

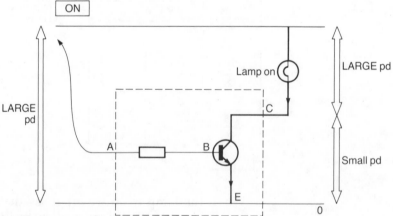

Figure 2.8

- when the input voltage is low (less than 0.5 V) the output voltage at the collector is high.

This is an **inversion** of voltages. The transistor used in this way is a **voltage inverter**. (Note that there is a range of uncertainty between 0.5 V and 0.7 V where the lamp is dim. We can't really say that it is on or off.) The system controls the lamp which acts as a load. The lamp can be exchanged for other kinds of load such as a motor or relay.

If you find the arguments above difficult, concentrate for the moment on the outcomes:

Low voltage at the input gives high voltage at the output and the lamp is off.
High voltage at the input gives low voltage at the output and the lamp is on.

*Making systems which are
sensitive to light or
temperature*

The aim now is to build some circuits which respond to changes in light
or temperature settings. We will continue to use the input and output
voltage levels as a way of sorting out how the systems behave.

Essentially, you set up a voltage divider circuit where one of the resistors is sensitive to light (or temperature) change. See, for example, fig 2.9
where an ldr (light-dependent resistor) is used. We said in Chapter 1 that
the voltage divider was a key arrangement in electronics. Here is an
example of its application.

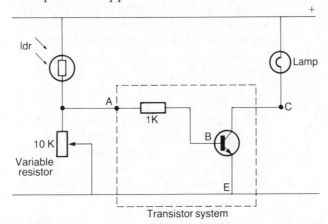

Figure 2.9

When the other resistance is a variable resistor ('pot'), you can adjust
the system to switch over at a particular light level. This gives you full
control of the system.
I suggest doing Activity 2.2 now.

Further consideration of the ldr circuit

The ldr and variable resistor form a voltage divider (fig 2.10). The voltage
level at A will change with the amount of light falling on the ldr.

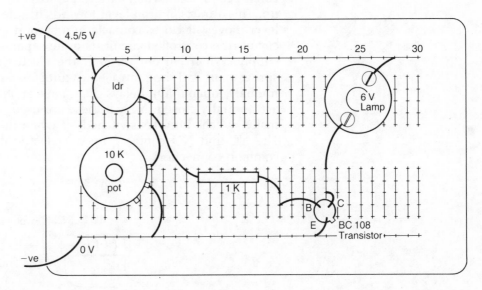

Figure 2.10

An argument for working out what should happen is:
When dark, the ldr has a high resistance. A large pd will be required to drive current through it; most of the available voltage difference will be used to do this. So, the voltage level at A will be small, possibly less than the 0.6 V required to switch the transistor on.

Remember that a low input to the transistor gives a high output. So, the voltage level at C will be high. There is no voltage difference to drive current through the lamp. Thus, the lamp is off. This theory should correspond to the findings in section 2 of Activity 2.2.

When bright, the ldr has a low resistance. Only a small voltage difference is needed to drive current through it and the voltage level at A is high. At the output side, voltage at C is low. This gives a large voltage difference to drive current through the lamp. So, the lamp is on. This kind of system could be used to control an advertising sign which would be on only during daylight hours. However, when the positions of the ldr and variable resistor in the circuit are exchanged the lamp is on when the ldr is dark. This system would be useful for putting lights on at night.

Using a relay

What does a relay do?

A **relay** is a mechanical switch which is electrically controlled. Unlike the transistor, it switches a circuit which can be electrically quite separate. It lets you control voltages which are different from those of the control circuit. For example, you could use a 5 V control supply to work a 12 V train set. You can even control alternating current.

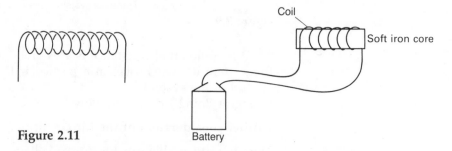

Figure 2.11

How does a relay work?

Relays contain an electromagnet. This is a coil of wire with a soft iron core. (See fig 2.11) When current passes through it, a magnetic field is set up. This attracts an iron lever towards the electromagnet (fig 2.12). As the lever moves, it closes contacts in a second circuit (fig 2.13). This second circuit (the controlled circuit) is quite separate and needs its own power supply. When current through the electromagnet ceases, the contacts spring apart and the controlled circuit is broken. These contacts are called **normally open** (NO). Relays often have another set of connections which are **normally closed** (NC). If these are used, any controlled circuit is normally switched on. It's switched off when the relay is activated (fig 2.14). The NC and NO contacts are not electrically isolated. They share one common connection.

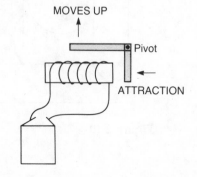

Figure 2.12

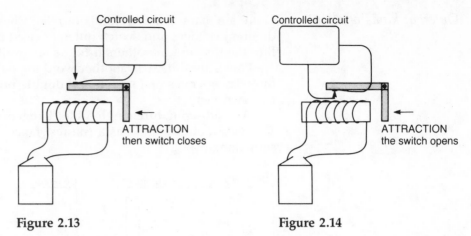

Figure 2.13   **Figure 2.14**

Activity 2.2

Making systems which are sensitive to light or temperature

The aim of this activity is to build systems which change with light or temperature settings.
You know that a transistor is switched on or off depending on the input voltage level. Can you make the input voltage sensitive to light (or temperature) change?

You need:
- 5 V low voltage dc supply
- transistor e.g. BC108 or ZTX300
- 1 K resistor
- 6 V (0.06 A) lamp in holder
- 10 K potentiometer ('pot')
- breadboard and correcting wires
- voltmeter (0–5 V)
- light dependent resistor (ldr) e.g. ORP12
- thermistor e.g. 2.2 K

Make one of these sensors (or ldr thermistor) part of a voltage divider circuit. Try the ldr first. The circuit is shown in fig 2.9. A breadboard layout is given in fig 2.10.

1 Can you adjust the variable resistor setting to make the system switch at an appropriate light level?
   When the ldr is dark (covered over) is your lamp on or off?

2 Use your voltmeter to show the input voltage at A (in fig 2.9) as you change the light level falling on the ldr.
   What do you find?
   Does it change in the way you expect?
   Can you complete the following?
   When the ldr is dark, the voltage at A is . . . This is a high/low input to the transistor. The output voltage at C is . . . This is high/low. The lamp is off/on. (Delete the word which is false).
   Can you think of a practical use for this kind of system?

3 What happens if you exchange the positions of the ldr and variable resistor?
   Can you think of a practical application for this circuit?

4 Now try the thermistor in place of the ldr.

Keep your circuit for future use.

Different kinds of relay

There are many different kinds of relay. They are designed to work from different voltages and switch different sized currents. I recommend three. Buy the first and the others if funds are available.

Pole is used here as another word for switch. **Single pole** means that the relay operates one switch and **double pole** means that it can operate two switches.

(1)   sub-miniature single pole changeover relay (RS 348–526).
This works on 5 V and has a coil resistance of 56 Ohm (fig 2.15). It costs something over £1.

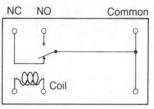
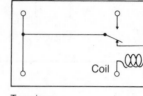

View from underneath (pin view)   Top view

Figure 2.15

Changeover means that there are both normally open (NO) and normally closed (NC) connections. The single pole switch has a common line which works between the NO and NC connections. This relay is particularly useful for switching a motor on and off, but acts rather more slowly than the reed relay.

(2)   sub-miniature double pole changeover (RS 346–851)
Double pole means that there are two switches which allows the relay to control two separate circuits (fig 2.16). It is useful for reversing motors and costs around £1.50.

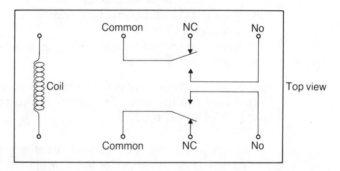

Figure 2.16

(3)   reed relay.
This is a fast acting single pole relay (RS 349–383) costing around £2 (fig 2.17). It requires only a small control current and can be worked directly from the NAND logic gates described later. It has a built-in diode to protect against induced back electromotive force (emf). For an explanation see page 00. However, you MUST make pin 2 +ve in the coil circuit. Otherwise, current will flow through the diode and short out the coil. Use the notch in the top of the chip to show which way round to connect it.

All these relays are **dual in line** (DIL). This means that they look like chips and will fit a breadboard or 2.5 mm stripboard. They all work on 5 V dc. Each can do the simple things but the second is the most versatile and will demonstrate latching.

Figure 2.17

Using a relay

Devices like relays and motors where the current gives rise to large magnetic fields must be used with care. When the magnetic fields change, large reverse voltages are often created known as 'back electromotive forces' (back emfs). A diode is used to provide a path for the 'induced' current. The diode must be connected the correct way round. It must not 'short out' the device. Activity 2.3 gives details of some practical work which can be done using a relay.

Activity 2.3

Using a relay

The aim is to see how a relay works and then to use one in a control circuit.
You will need:
- 5 V sub-miniature relay (single pole changeover)
- 4.5/5 V dc supply (battery or low voltage supply)
- 3.5 V lamp in holder
- breadboard and connections
- transistor e.g. BC108
- diode (IN4001)
- variable resistor (10 K)
- ldr (ORP12)
- (optional – multimeter measuring Ohms)

Look at your relay. The simplest has only 4 connections but yours has more. Two will link with the coil. When current passes through the coil, it has a magnetic effect which causes the switches to open and close.

1 Your lamp will light when you select connections between the common and normally closed (NC) contacts.

2 It will remain out when connected between the common and normally open (NO) contacts.

3 When the circuit is connected to the coil connections you should hear a small click as the relay switches. You may be surprised that the lamp does not light. The coil has a resistance of some tens of ohms and needs only a small current to make it work. This current is not usually large enough to light the lamp.

4 To check the common to NO contacts, you will need to activate the coil and test whether the connections have closed.
(If you use an ohm-meter it will show a moderate resistance when connected across the coil, almost zero when connected between the common and NC contacts and a very high value across the common and NO contacts.)
Use fig 2.15 to identify the pin connections for your relay. Test the connections by using a 4.5 V battery linked in series with a 3.5 V lamp (fig 2.18).

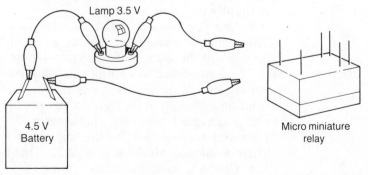

Lamp 3.5 V

4.5 V
Battery

Micro miniature
relay

Figure 2.18

Activity 2.3 continued

*Switching a relay using a
light sensitive control
circuit*

You have already built a transistor system which is sensitive to light in Activity 2.2 (figs 2,9 and 2.10).

To work a relay, simply replace the lamp with the relay coil. Then, connect a lamp which can be controlled by the relay. (It could be powered by a separate supply, but it is probably more convenient to use the same supply.) If you think that introducing the relay hasn't achieved very much, you could be right. The point is that you could, if you wished, control the lamp with a completely separate voltage supply. The circuit diagram is shown in fig 2.19 and the breadboard layout in fig 2.20. (Note that the diode has been included as 'good practice' when using a relay).

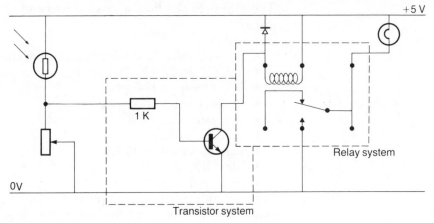

Figure 2.19

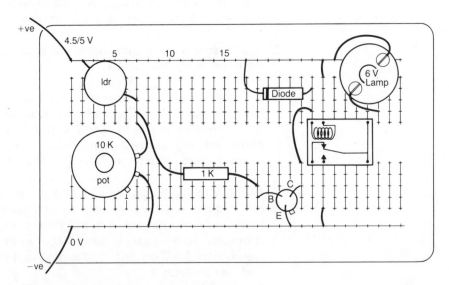

Figure 2.20

- Can you make the system work?

A slightly different problem.

- Can you make the relay switch a lamp on when it gets dark?

This principle could be useful for street lights! It is mainly a matter of sorting out the relay pins and consolidating your ideas.

To a transistor to control the relay coils you need to use a 4.5 V battery or 5 V dc supply for both transistor and controlled circuit. A solution is shown in fig 2.21. As you set up your circuit, check that the coil is activated when the transistor base goes to 'high' voltage. The transistor is 'switched' by the ldr and this in turn controls the relay. There is another solution in fig 2.22. This uses the NC connections.

- Can you make this work?

Keep your circuit for Activities 2.4 and 2.5.　　*Activity 2.3 continued*

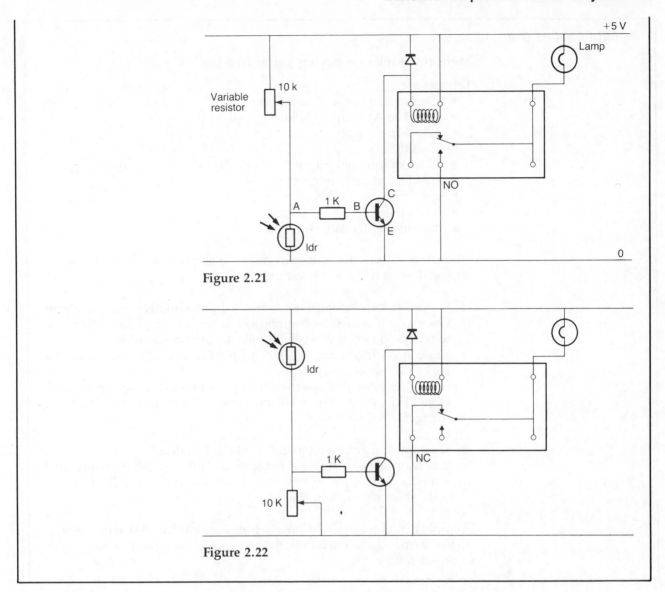

Figure 2.21

Figure 2.22

Two further points

1.   Systems
You can also regard the relay as a system. What you have done is to make the transistor and the relay **sub-systems** of a larger one.

2.   Using a transistor
The current passing through the relay coil **sinks** into the transistor collector. This is the normal way of using npn transistors. (So far, we have only used the npn type.) See page 34 for further discussion on sinking current.

Using a relay to make a 'latch'

When you 'latch onto' an idea you stick with it until someone persuades you otherwise. A door lock is 'latched' when you want to hold it in place. **Latching** is also used in electronics. In this context it means holding the output voltage of a system until something happens to change it. A straightforward demonstration of latching can be set up using a double pole changeover relay. Practical details are given in Activity 2.4

Some practical problems

Up to now we have been using control systems which respond to light changes and operate a lamp as the load. By exchanging the ldr for a thermistor the system can be made sensitive to temperature. By exchanging the lamp for a motor a system you can control a mechanical load. Activity 2.5 gives an opportunity to try these out by solving some practical problems. The third problem, preventing a candle being lit, extends into mechanisms. Clearly this must be undertaken with care.

Activity 2.4 (optional).

More about relays – staying put or latching

This needs:
- relay (double pole changeover)
- 6 V (0.06 A) lamp in holder
- 4.5/5 V dc supply
- ldr (ORP12)
- 10 K potentiometer (pot)
- breadboard and connections
- transistor e.g. BC108
- 1 K resistor
- didode e.g. IN4001

When the current through a relay coil changes, so does the switch setting. This is not always wanted.

1 Suppose, for example, you want a **light-sensitive burglar alarm**. Once a light beam has been broken it sets off an alarm. This needs to remain on even when light falls on the sensor again.
You can do this using the second pole of a double pole relay. Fig 2.23 shows how to do it.
When the relay coil is activated a path to earth is set up through PQR. This keeps the relay on, even when the original setting changes.

2 The light sensor arrangement needs to be added.
It is really quite a clever arrangement. You may have already built a similar circuit, if you built the circuit shown in fig 2.20. Can you make this one work in practice?

Control circuits which hold their settings are called LATCHED circuits. It's like a front door where a latch can be used keep the lock in its open or closed setting.

Activity 2.5

Some practical problems using sensors heat and light sensors

You need some something like the following, depending on your problem and proposed solution.
- 5 V low voltage dc supply
- transistor BC108 or ZTX300
- 1 K resistor
- 6 V (0.06 A) lamp in holder
- 10 K potentiometer ('pot')
- relay (double pole changeover)
- 5 V electric motor
- 2 diodes (IN4001)
- thermistor
- ldr
- breadboard and connecting wires
- small birthday candle and matches
- possibly, thread, plasticine, garden-wire, propeller, aluminium foil, plastic pots and other generally available items/junk
- glue gun
- voltmeter (0–5 V) (for fault finding)

Activity 2.5 continued

1 High temperature alarm

Can you modify the circuits shown in figs 2.21 or 2.22 to switch the lamp on when the temperature is high?
Can you vary the switching temperature?
How would you make the lamp switch on at low temperature?

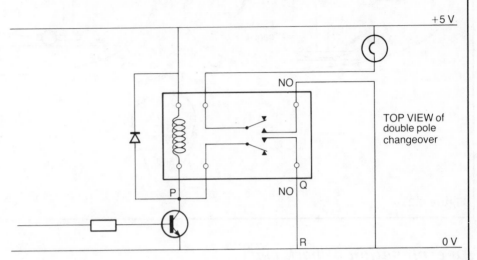

Figure 2.23

2 Controlling a motor

Can you develop this circuit to make the relay control a motor?
Do not forget to add a diode across your motor. This will protect against back emfs. Work out which way round. Can you make it work? See fig 2.24.

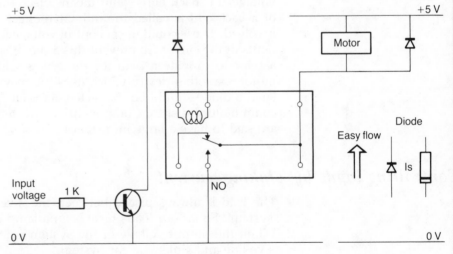

Figure 2.24

3 Can you design and build a system which stops you lighting a candle?

In other words, when you try to light a candle, something happens to put the flame out.
One solution might be to use an ldr to detect the light or a thermistor to detect the heat from a match and then switch on some action which stops the candle being lit.
Try and devise as many different solutions as you can. Look at other people's solutions and try to be different. See fig 2.25 for some ideas.
Some of the possible solutions to these problems can be found on page 36.

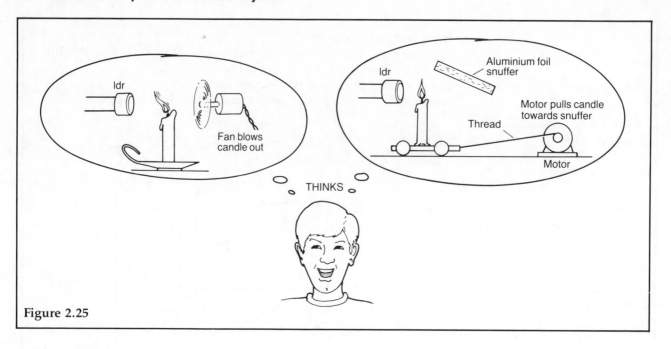

Figure 2.25

An explanation of back emf

Electric voltages are 'induced' whenever the magnetic fields which are linked with a circuit change. In a relay switch the current through the coil sets up a magnetic field. This magnetic field holds energy. When current in the coil is switched off this energy is released and can generate a backward surge of current. The energy released tries to maintain the current through the coil.

The voltages generated by this backward surge are known as 'induced' voltages or '**back emfs**' (emf means electromotive force). The generation of a back emf is called the inductive effect. Quite high voltages can be involved. These could upset control voltage levels or even damage components in the circuit. To prevent this a diode is connected across the coil of a relay to provide a path for the reverse 'induced' current. An electric motor is another device which uses the magnetic field of a current. Similarly, a diode should be connected across it. This reduces sparking at the commutator brushes. Components which tend to given a large back emf are said to have a large inductance.

Controlling loads by 'sinking' current

The load is always placed between the +ve line and the output of the 'system'. So far our loads have been a lamp or a motor.
When the output voltage of the system is low, a current flows from the +ve line and **sinks** into the system.

Figure 2.26

We will meet other systems which sink the load current. Examples are the Darlington pair (Chapter 3) and logic gates (Chapter 4).
Some systems can **source** current. Here the output supplies current to the load which is placed between the output and earth, as shown in fig 2.26.

Control systems which sink current are much more common than ones which source if the transistors which we have used up to now work in this way. They are known as npn transistors. However, there is another kind called pnp transistors. These work by sourcing current. In contrast to npn transistors, they switch on when the input voltage is low and off when the input voltage level is high. We will use one to reverse a motor in Chapter 6.

Summary

In a systems approach you concentrate on input and output voltages. You are more concerned about what a system does rather than how it does it. It is a powerful way of dealing electrical with systems. (fig 2.27)

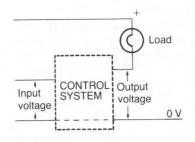

Figure 2.27

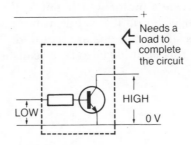

Figure 2.28

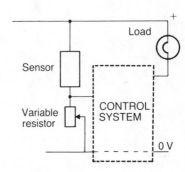

Figure 2.29

If you treat a single transistor as a system, it converts low voltage to high and vice versa. It acts as a voltage inverter. (fig 2.28)

A sensor such as a ldr or thermistor as part of a voltage divider on the input side makes a system sensitive to light or temperature. (fig 2.29)

A relay switch can be included in a control system to make it work an electrically separate circuit. (fig 2.30)

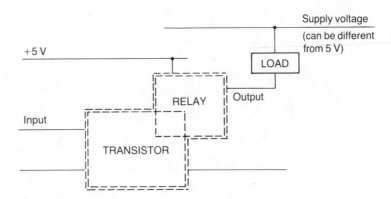

Figure 2.30

A changeover relay has NO (normally open) and NC (normally closed) connections.

Diodes are connected across inductive loads to prevent back emf's affecting the circuit (e.g. sparking between contacts at separation).

Control circuits normally **sink** load current.

Solutions

Activity 2.5

1 **The high temperature alarm** can be made by changing the ldr for a thermistor.

The critical temperature to switch the system will depend on the variable resistor setting.

There are two ways of changing the 'sense' in which the circuit works. Either – exchange the position of the thermistor and variable resistor or, swap the NO and NC connections on the relay.

2 **Keeping a candle unlit**

You could use an ldr or a thermistor as a sensor.

There are many ways of keeping the candle unlit. Some examples are:

(a) Switch on a fan which blows the flame out.

(b) Activate a motor to knock the candle over.

(c) Activate a motor which 'snufs' the flame out.

(d) Pour water on it . . . but, water and electricity is a dangerous mix. Special precautions are required! Use only battery power. In practice this is unlikely to be a realistic solution.

3 Controlling larger currents: using relays, transistors and Darlington Drivers

Introduction

We have already seen how transistors and relays can control small currents (about 0.1 A) by switching a small lamp on and off. However, if you want to control movement using a motor, much higher currents can be involved. An electric motor which is under a heavy load or stalled carries a high current and the circuit needs to be able to cope with this.

In this chapter we will deal with practical ways of controlling larger currents of 0.5 A or more. A relay could be used as we saw in the previous chapter. This is a mechanical solution. Alternatively, a high current transistor or Darlington driver could be used. This is a solid state method. The use of solid state solutions to control larger currents will be discussed in some detail in this chapter. Also, the advantages and disadvantages of using relays or solid state switches are mentioned. A systems approach will continue to be used.

Controlling larger currents with transistors

Different kinds of transistor The transistors which you have used up to now are designed to control relatively small current (up to 0.5 A). However, higher current transistors are readily available. Supplier's catalogues have a bewildering array of transistors. The table below shows a small selection from the RS catalogue.

	type	I_c	gain (h_{fe})	case	V_{CEO}	approx price
1	BC108	100 mA	110–800	TO18	30 V	20p
2	ZTX300	500 mA	50–300	E-line	25 V	15p
3	BFY51	1 A	40	TO39	60 V	25p
4	TIP31A	3 A	10–60	TO220	60 V	40p
5	TIP33A	10 A	20–100	TAB	60 V	80p
6	MJ2501	10 A	1000	TO3	80 V	£2
7	TIP141	10 A	1000	TAB	80 V	£2

I_c is the collector curent. This is effectively the current which can be controlled by the transistor. Devices which can control high current (10 A or so) are more expensive than those which control small currents.

The collector current is controlled by a much smaller current flowing into the base. The ratio between collector and base current is the **gain** (h_{fe}). It appears from the table that there are two types of transistor. The first five have a modest gain usually no more than 100. The last two have a rather higher gain. The high gain units are known as Darlingtons. They are a special arrangement of two transistors and are discussed in more detail on page 40.

Transistors are built into cases of different shape and size. The reference is given in the column headed **case**. You will have to consult a supplier's catalogue to find the meaning of each reference. You can also use the supplier's catalogue to find out the pin connections. See fig 3.1.

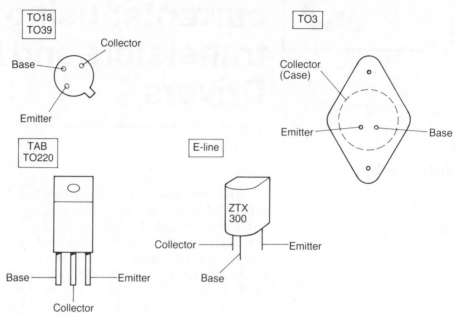

Figure 3.1

The V_{CEO} of a transistor indicates the maximum operating voltage between the collector and the emitter. In practice it can be regarded as the maximum supply voltage. The transistors listed in the table can be used in any of the circuits made so far.

Heat sink for a high current transistor

When a large current is passed through a transistor, it gets hot. They are designed to do this and a **heat sink** is sometimes added. The heat sink is a small sheet of metal clamped to the transistor (fig 3.2). It prevents overheating by dissipating the heat to the surrounding air.

Building a permanent connecting system for a high current transistor

A permanent circuit using a high current transistor may be useful if high currents need to be controlled, for example, with an electromagnet or points in a train set.

The system can be conveniently built using barrel terminal blocks glue-gunned to a wood base (fig 3.3). A small amount of soldering is required.

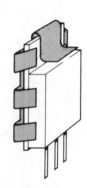

Figure 3.2

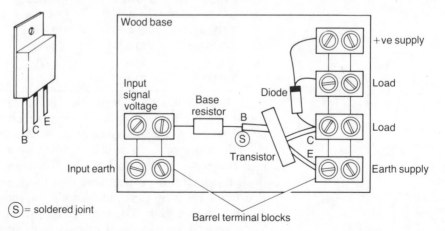

Figure 3.3

You have a decision to make about which transistor to use. The TIP31A is suitable for most applications. However, if you can afford it, use a TIP141.

Activity 3.1 should be regarded as optional. I suggest that you delay building the system until you need to use it.

Activity 3.1 – (optional)

Building a permanent system for a high current transistor
You need:
- high current transistor and resistor, e.g. TIP31A and 330 R or TIP141 and 1 K
- barrel terminal block (RS 423–554)
- diode IN5401 (carries 3 A)
- small wood block
- connecting wire
- soldering iron and a glue gun

This system can control high current through a load connected as shown in fig 3.4.

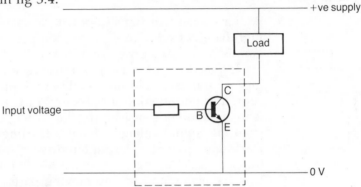

Figure 3.4

You should be able to build it by using fig 3.3. Take care to identify the transistor pins correctly. They are the same for both the TIP31A and the TIP141. Note that a diode has been added across the load.

Choosing a transistor: calculating the base current

The choice of a transistor for a particular job depends on the size of the current which is to be controlled. For example, suppose you want to control a current of 0.3 A, from the table a TIP31A transistor looks as if it would be suitable (fig 3.5). However, the base current that will be required needs to be found out and also whether the controlling circuit can supply it. Assume that the base to collector gain (h_{fe}) is 60.

(a) What base current would be required?
The solution can be worked out from the value for gain.

$$\text{gain} = \frac{\text{Collector current}}{\text{Base current}}$$

If gain = 60 and collector current = 3 A
$$\text{then } 60 = \frac{3}{\text{Base current}}$$

Base current = 3/60
$$= 0.05 \text{ A} = 50 \text{ mA (I)}$$

If this base current is available, the value for the base resistor can be calculated.

(b) Suppose the transistor is to be switched on by a voltage of +5 V. What base resistor is needed?

Assume that a voltage difference of 5 V is available to drive current into base. You need to work out what value of resistor will allow a current of 50 mA to pass.

$$using V = IR$$
$$gives 5 = 50/1000 \times R$$
$$so R = 5 \times 1000/50 = 100\,Ohm$$

Compared with our introduction to the use of a transistor, the base resistor is small and the base current quite large. It may not be possible for the control circuit supply to be as much as 50 mA for the transistor base. In this case use a TIP141 transistor which has a much larger gain (1000). This device would require a much smaller base current (3 mA) to control 3 A. Using the same method as above you can show that the base resistor would be 1.3 K. In fact the TIP141 is a Darlington pair of transistors. Darlington pairs are described in the next section.

The Darlington pair

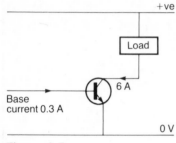

Figure 3.5

We have seen that transistors with a relatively small gain require quite a high base current. For example, suppose we wish to control 6 A. If the gain is 20, a base current of $6/20 = 0.3$ A is needed, see fig 3.5

In practice, this is a large control current. Many control circuits including computers would not be able to supply it. A typical current from a computer output control is about 2 mA. A way of solving the problem t is to use another transistor (fig 3.6). Then, only a small current is required from the control voltage. This is a **Darlington arrangement** (also called a **Darlington pair** or a **Darlington driver**). A Darlington pair consists of two transistors. A Darlington system is used to switch reasonably high currents. It is fast acting and has no moving parts. This means that it can switch on and off very rapidly without mechanical fatigue – something a relay cannot do. It has a rather more definite on/off than a single transistor, as a very small change in voltage level around the critical value switches it on or off.

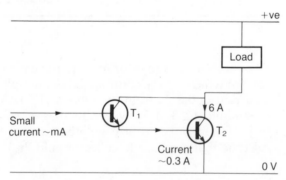

Figure 3.6

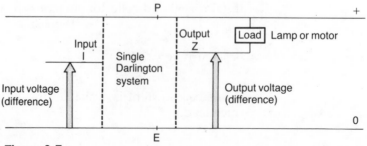

Figure 3.7

A single Darlington has the following connections (fig 3.7):

I – input line. The voltage switches the Darlington
Z – output line. This is connected through the load (e.g. lamp, relay or motor) to the positive line

The Darlington controls how much current passes through the load. It 'sinks' current. A diode is included in the system for use with inductive loads such as motors. The Darlington system needs to be linked to the positive (P) and earth (E) lines. The components inside the system are shown in fig 3.8 and the logic symbol representation for a Darlington is shown in fig 3.9.

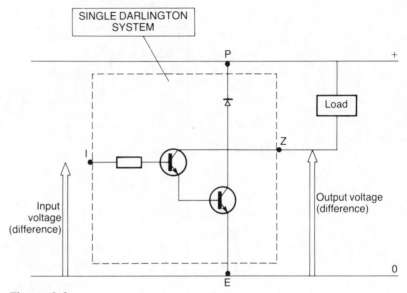

Figure 3.8

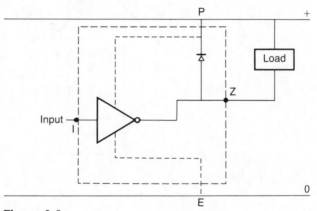

Figure 3.9

Details of how to build a Darlington are given in Activity 3.2. However, if you just want to use a Darlington, the combination is available as an integrated circuit. This can be bought as a single system, e.g. TIP141 or MJ2501, or as a set of eight Darlingtons in a chip.

Activity 3.3 gives details of how to use a Darlington in a chip. I suggest that this is regarded as the mainstream activity and the building of a Darlington as an optional extra.

Activity 3.2 (optional)

Building a Darlington from components

A Darlington can be built as shown (figs 3.10 and 3.11). Transistor BFY51 can carry a current up to 1 A from collector to emitter. The BC108 is a common or garden general purpose (npn) transistor. It carries a rather smaller current – up to 0.1 A.

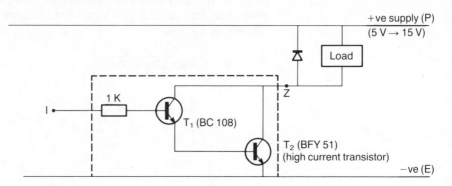

Figure 3.10

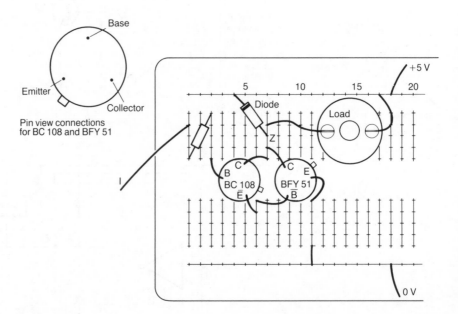

Figure 3.11

You need:
- transistor BFY51 (high current)(RS293–640)
- transistor BC108
- 1 K resistor
- 6 V (0.06 A) lamp in holder or low voltage motor
- diode IN4001
- voltmeter (0–5 V)
- 5 V and 9 V dc supply
- 10 K variable resistor
- breadboard and connections

Activity 3.2 continued

Activity 3.2

Some questions

1 When the input (at I) is at high voltage, does a large current flow through the load? In other words, is the system on?
2 The output from the system is at 'Z'. When the input (at I) is high, is the voltage at Z high or low?
3 A single transistor switches on when the base voltage is greater than 0.6 V (approx). What is the critical voltage (at I) which changes the Darlington system? Is it the same as for a single transistor? (Add the 10 K variable resistor to give you a variable voltage at I.)
4 The supply voltage to some Darlington systems can be increased to as much as 50 V. If your supply voltage is increased to 9 V, does the critical input voltage remain the same?

Activity 3.3

Darlington drivers in a chip using a Darlington to control current

You can buy 8 Darlington drivers in a single chip – costing under £2. A single driver circuit can control a current up to 0.5 A. To control a larger current, Darlingtons can be linked together in parallel. Each then carries part of the total current.

You need:

- 'octal' chip with 8 Darlingtons
- 5 V (and optional 9 V) dc supply
- 2 lamps (6 V, 0.06 A) in holders
- breadboard and connecting wires
- dc voltmeter (0–9 V)
- 10 K variable resistor
- 1 K resistor
- ldr ORP12·
- 4/5 V electric motor
- dc ammeter (0–10 A)

You need to sort out a single Darlington system in the chip. Compare fig 3.8, 3.12 and 3.13. Make sure you can identify the marker notch on top of the chip. Use this to identify the pin numbers.

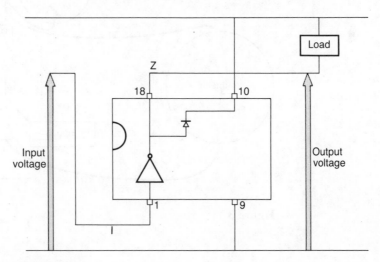

Figure 3.12

Activity 3.3 continued

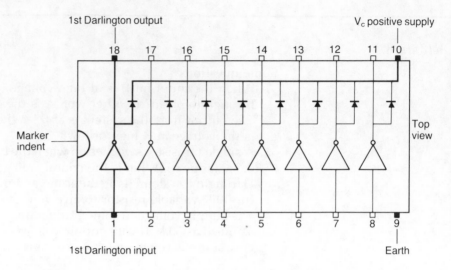

Figure 3.13

Single Darlington connections		pin connections on chip
I	[1]	Input for 1st Darlington
P	[10]	V_c Positive supply. The chip has built-in diodes for inductive loads
Z	[18]	Output for 1st Darlington. The 'load' is connected between 18 and positive supply
E	[9]	Earth connection

Plug your chip into the breadboard as shown in fig 3.14. Connect a 5 V supply voltage (+ve to pin 10, −ve to 9). Select the first Darlington circuit in your chip and connect a 6 V lamp as load between pin 18 and the +ve supply.

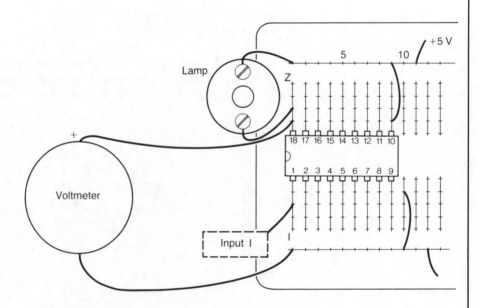

Figure 3.14

Activity 3.3 continued

1 **Input and output voltages**.
   Connect the input I (pin 1 for first Darlington) to high and then to low voltage and see how this affects the output. Use a voltmeter to measure the output voltage levels.
   a) What is the relation between input and output voltage? Low will be approx 0 V, high will be around 5 V.
   b) If the input voltage (pin 1) is low, what is the output voltage (pin 18)? Is the lamp on or off? Complete a table like the one shown in fig 3.15.

Input voltage	Output voltage	Lamp on/off
Low		
High		

Figure 3.15

2 **Critical input voltage**
   Connect the variable resistor as shown in figs 3.16 and 3.17. Change the voltmeter connections to measure the input voltage level.
   a) Find the critical value of the input voltage which will just switch the lamp on. Is it around 0.6 V, as with a single transistor?
   b) If you have time, investigate whether the critical value for the input voltage changes if the supply voltage is changed. Try using 9 V.

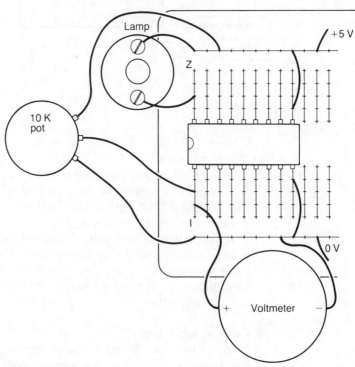

Figure 3.16

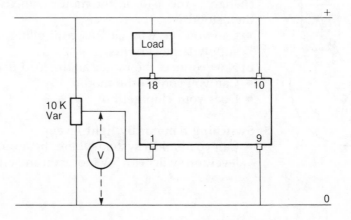

Figure 3.17

Activity 3.3 continued

3 Linking two Darlingtons

Continue by using a 5 V supply.

- Can you reverse the system logic so that a high input voltage produces a high output voltage?

This can be done by combining two sets of Darlingtons.

Arrange for the output from one to be the input to another. You can use two lamps – one for each Darlington. See fig 3.18. To avoid confusion, it would be better to change the first lamp for a 1 K resistor.

- Does the system still work?
- Why doesn't this resistor get hot like the lamp?

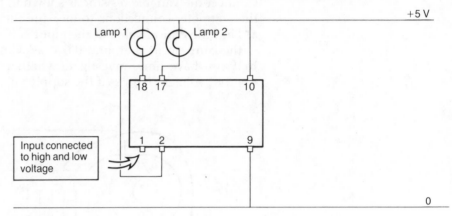

Figure 3.18

3a Open collector

This is an advanced point which you can skip over first time round. If you get the reverse logic circuit to work, try removing the load from the first Darlington. This will be a lamp or 1 K resistor.

- Does the system still work?

If it does, it will be because the output of the first Darlington is linked to the positive supply through the internal diode. The diode completes a voltage divider even if the load is removed.

The output of a system is often called the **collector**. This is by analogy with a single transistor.

4 Controlling a motor

Find out how much current passes through a motor to make it work. Measure the current by linking a motor and ammeter (0–10 A) in series.

Connect these directly to the supply (fig 3.19). How does the current change as the load on the motor is increased to slow it down and then stop it?

- Can you see why circuits controlling motors need to be able to supply large currents?

b) Now connect the motor as the load using the Darlington chip.

- Can you control the motor?
- Does your chip get hot?

5 Switching a motor by light level

- Can you build a system where the input voltage depends on light level and switches a 5 V motor on and off? Use a 4.5/5 V supply.

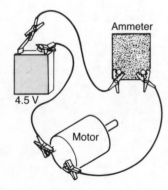

Figure 3.19

Solutions to these problems can be found on page 51.

Activity 3.4 (optional)

Making a permanent connecting system for chips
Many systems come in 'chip' sized packages. So far we have met Darlingtons and relays. Later on logic gates in chip form will be used. Breadboard has limitations for more permanent connections. One convenient, cheap and reliable way of getting at the chip connections is to use 'barrel terminal blocks'. If 4 mm terminal blocks are used every size of plug up to 4 mm can be connected, as well as bare wires. It is not essential to have such a system, but it is sometimes useful for investigations and control projects. Use stripboard for the base and a chip socket to allow you to change the chip. I suggest that you build this only when required.
You need:
- 4 mm terminal blocks (RS 423–554)
- 18-way chip sockets (RS 402–204)
- a small piece of stripboard base (RS 433–826)
- connecting wires

Refer to fig 3.20 if you want some help.

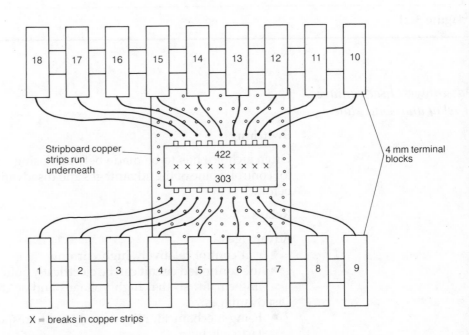

Figure 3.20

The strips run underneath in direction ⟵——⟶.
Break the strip connections at the points marked **X** (9 in total).
Solder single strand connecting wires to the stripboard.
The terminal blocks can be 'glue gunned' to the base.

Activity 3.4 continued

A simpler system for connecting to the single pole relay is shown in fig 3.21. A 14-way chip socket is useful here (RS 401–790).

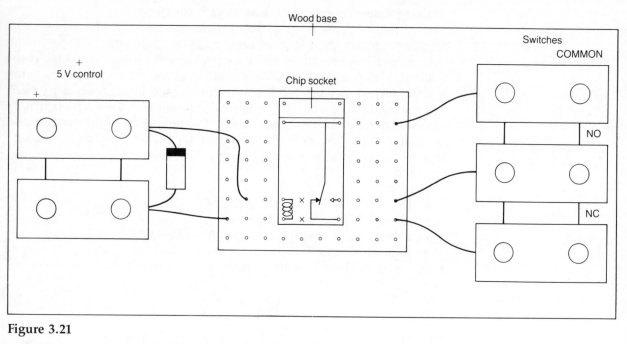

Figure 3.21

Advantages/disadvantages
of relay and solid state

Switching

Often a choice has to be made between using a relay or solid state switch for control. Some of the advantages and disadvantages are brought together below.

Relays

Advantages:
- can control relatively high currents
- the controlled circuit can be electrically quite separate from the control-ling circuit, so that high voltages and ac can be controlled

Disadvantages:
- being mechanical, relays need time to respond – they cannot do very fast switching.
- mechanical parts have limited life

Solid state switches (e.g. transistor, Darlington)

Advantages:
- can also control high current
- respond very quickly
- there is no mechanical fatigue and should last a long time

Disadvantages:
- maximum voltage which can be switched is 50 V*
- cannot control ac
- cannot conveniently change current direction, e.g. reversing a motor

The Darlington pair gives a more precise switching action than a single transistor.

*This is only true for simple systems. Solid state components have been developed to overcome these limitations.

Summary

1 Both relays and transistors can control fairly high current, over 0.5 A.
2 Transistors act as a 'solid state' switch, with no moving parts.
3 The Darlington has two transistors and acts as a high current 'solid state' switch. A very small input current can control a high current, 0.5 A and more. The switching action is more precise than a single transistor.
4 Transistors and Darlingtons act as voltage inverters.
5 Relays give electrical separation between controlling and controlled circuits but are slow acting and suffer mechanical fatigue.
6 Solid state switches are fast acting and long lasting.
7 Barrel terminal blocks make a convenient 'universal' system for making connections.

Consolidation questions

1 In a model house, warm air needs to be circulated when the temperature is low. The circuit shown in fig 3.22 was built to switch on a fan at low temperature. (At low temperature, the thermistor has a high resistance.) It does not work.
How many design faults and misconnections can you find?

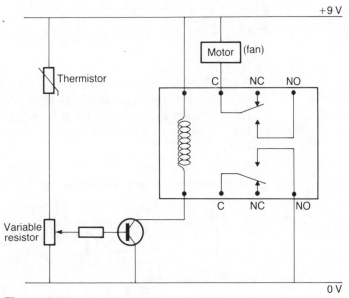

Figure 3.22

2 Draw a circuit diagram to show how you would use a high current transistor instead of a relay to do the same job as question 1.

3 Fig 3.23 shows a relay controlling a lamp. Treating it as a system, work out how the input (at I) controls the output voltage (at Z).

Input voltage (at I)	Output voltage (at Z)	Lamp on/off
Low (approx 0 V)		
High (approx 5 V)		

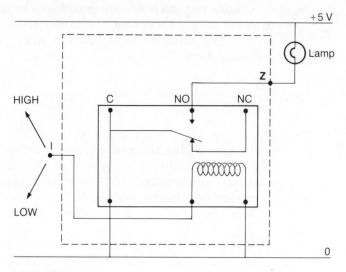

Figure 3.23

4 Fig 3.23 shows two control systems each of which uses two transistors. In each case, the second transistor T_2 can carry high current.
(i) Which is a Darlington arrangement?
(ii) List as many differences as you can in the way each system works.

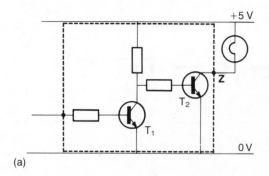

(a)

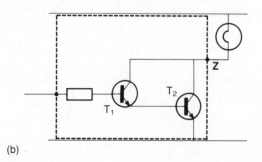

(b)

Figure 3.24

5 An octal Darlington chip is being used to control a lamp. Only one of the internal circuits is in use (fig 3.25).

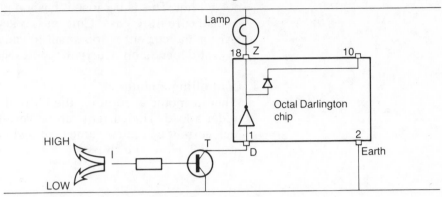

Figure 3.25

(i) In building the circuit the link between pin 10 and the +ve supply line has been omitted.
   • Will the circuit work? Can you explain why?
(ii) The Darlington acts as an inverter.
   • What happens at the output (Z) when the voltage level at I changes?

Answers are given on page 52.

Solutions

Activity 3.3

1 **Input and output voltages**
People usually find:

input voltage (I)	output voltage (Z)	lamp
low	high	off
high	low	on

If you do not agree, check that you are measuring the output voltage between earth and the Darlington output at Z. Notice from these results that, like a single transistor, the Darlington acts as a voltage inverter.

2 **Critical voltage input**
The critical input voltage to switch the Darlington is about 1.4 V. People with experience of linking two transistors in other ways may find this result unexpected. In the Darlington system the critical voltages of the invidivual transistors add together (fig 3.26). The critical voltage does not change very much if the supply voltage is altered. Did you find the Darlington a 'snappy switcher'? Very small changes in voltage level around the critical value switch it on or off. This makes it more sensitive than single transistor control.

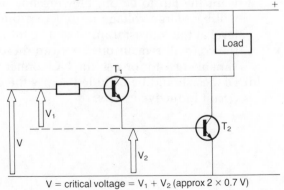

Figure 3.26 V = critical voltage = $V_1 + V_2$ (approx 2×0.7 V)

3 Linking two Darlingtons

When the 'load' is a 1 K resistor instead of a lamp or motor, it does not get hot. This is because it has a high resistance which allows only a small current to pass. Current is a key factor in heating. With a 1 K resistor the current is too small to cause much heating. The amount of heat depends on $(Current)^2 \times$ Resistance, i.e. I^2R.

4 Controlling a motor

When a motor is running the current increases as the motor slows under a load. The current can be very large if the motor is stalled. A high current will cause some heating in the Darlington chip. Too much heat will 'blow' the chip.

Consolidation questions

1 The revised circuit is shown in fig 3.27

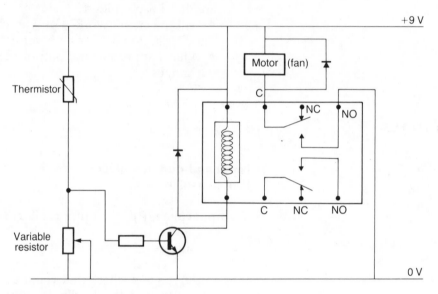

Figure 3.27

(a) The NO connection of the top switch (not the bottom one) needs to be connected to earth. When the switch is activated, there is a path to earth through the fan.

(b) The voltage divider control circuit (made up of thermistor and variable resistor) is unusual. It may work. Connecting between the end and centre tap of the variable resistor as shown in fig 3.27 will give a greater change in the voltage level.

(c) Is the thermistor in the right place?

At low temperature the thermistor has a large resistance. We want the fan to be on, blowing hot air around the house. There will be a large voltage drop across the thermistor, so the voltage level at the transistor input will be low, its output will be high and the coil will remain off. So swap the positions of thermistor and variable resistor or use the NC connection.

(d) Diodes should be included across the coil and the motor to short circuit inductive effects.

2 A transistor circuit is shown in fig 3.28

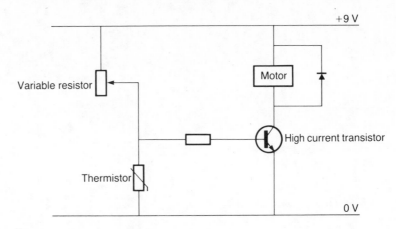

Figure 3.28

3 The table should be:

Input voltage (at I)	Output voltage (at Z)	Lamp on/off
Low (approx 0 V)	high	off
High (approx 5 V)	low	on

When the input at I is low, the relay is off. No current flows through the lamp and Z is at high voltage.

When I is taken to high voltage, current flows through the coil and the relay is switched on. The contact between NO and C is closed. Z goes to zero voltage and the lamp goes on. The system acts as a voltage inverter (low at I, high at Z).

4 (a) Fig 3.26 is the Darlington
 (b) Some differences are:
  In (a), all current through the load travels through transistor T_2. In (b) it is shared between T_1 and T_2. In (a) 0.6 V at I will switch the system but in (b), a higher voltage is needed (approx. 1.4 V). In (a) high voltage input gives high output level at Z. In (b) the system is a voltage inverter.

5 (a) The circuit will work. Pin 18 provides a path to 'sink' the load current through the chip. Pin 10 connects to a diode. If linked to the +ve supply it provides a path around the load for back emf. This is a precaution for inductive loads.
 (b) A high voltage at the input (I) makes the Darlington input (D) low. The Darlington output at Z is HIGH and the lamp off.

4 | Electronics and logic

Introduction

In this chapter we will continue with a systems approach. We will look at the way in which HIGH and LOW voltage in an electric circuit can be linked with TRUE and FALSE in a logic approach. This leads to a way of solving practical problems using electric circuits. The first part of the chapter gives an introduction to logic gates and refers to circuits which we have used already. You can set these up and test whether they behave as described. However, the main practical activity is directed towards using logic gates in a chip.

A logic approach

Electronic systems

We have already treated electric circuits as a system. You look at the inputs and outputs and do not need to worry too much about why the circuit works. The key idea here is that the input can only take **one** of **two distinct 'states'** – HIGH voltage or LOW voltage. The same is true for the output. Up to now, our electronic systems have worked with only one input. Now we will see how to operate with more than one input.

Logic gates

Figure 4.1

A logic gate consists of a complete circuit, including transistors and other components inside an integrated circuit.
A **gate** can be open or closed (fig 4.1). When logic gates are open, information can pass through and affect the output.

Boolean algebra

Over a hundred years ago the mathematician George Boole invented a system of logic based on truth. In this system only **one** of **two** answers is allowed e.g.
- either you are hot or you are cold
- either you are female or male
- either you are alive or dead.

On this basis, he invented a system of algebra now called Boolean algebra. It is different from ordinary algebra in having only two states **true** or **false**. As electronics has developed it has been realised that Boole's ideas have a ready application. For example, a switch is either **on** or **off**. Transistors are **on** or **off** under electrical control. These give rise to two states.

If you swap **true** and **false** for **high** and **low voltage**, you have two **states** which can apply to electrical circuits.
With only two states, you need just two numbers to represent them, 0 and 1. This is binary notation and I'm sure you've heard that it's useful for electric circuits.

Logic state and voltage level

A voltage level can be linked with a logic state. The precise voltage level is not important. What really matters is whether it is above or below a critical value. Below the critical level is state 0 and above it is state 1. (e.g. for a transistor, the critical input voltage level is around 0.6 V. Above this, the input state is 1. Below it, the state is 0)

Boolean algebra is concerned with truth statements.
False is state 0 and **true** is state 1.
So, we have

TRUTH STATEMENT	ELECTRICAL EQUIVLALENT voltage level	LOGIC VALUE
false	low	0
true	high	1

To see how Boolean algebra works, consider an example. **IF** Joan is older than 17 **then** she can vote. Suppose Joan is 18. The answer to 'Is Joan older than 17?' is Yes. The input is **true** and this has logic value of 1.
The output state is that Joan can vote. This also has logic value of 1. The relationship between input and output can be shown in a **truth table**. For Joan voting it would be:

Truth Table

Input	output
Joan > 17?	can she vote?
0	0
1	1

0=yes 1=no

Electric circuits can be built which model this behaviour using input and output voltage levels.

Consider another example. Suppose that when Joan is over 17 she will NOT get pocket money.

input	output
Joan > 17?	does she get pocket money?
0	1
1	0

This is called a NOT relation or inversion of the input. It can be modelled easily using a transistor. Inversion of the input has been discussed in earlier chapters.

The inverter or NOT gate

Transistor as a NOT gate

You should already be familiar with using a transistor as a switch. In the circuit shown in figure 4.2 the input voltage at I sets up an output voltage at Z.

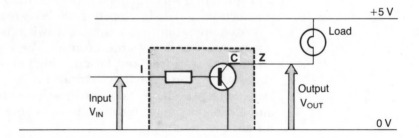

Figure 4.2

The value at 'Z' controls whether the lamp is on or off.
The table shows the relationship between voltage, logic state and the condition of the lamp (on or off).

Input		Output		Lamp
voltage	logic	voltage	logic	
Low (< 0.6 V)	0	High (approx 5 V)	1	Off
High (> 0.6 V)	1	Low (approx 0.5 V)	0	On

The transistor system inverts the logic i.e. 0 becomes 1 and 1 becomes 0. This is called an inverter (fig 4.3). In logic, it is called a NOT gate. Remember that there are only two states. A '**low**' voltage at the input is turned into a '**NOT low**' at the output . . . in other words, it becomes high. In the same way a **high** input voltage becomes a '**NOT high**' . . . i.e. a low voltage.

Figure 4.3

Darlington as a NOT gate

The Darlington circuit also acts as a voltage **inverter** (fig 4.4). This circuit was studied in Chapter 3. The symbol for a NOT gate is shown in fig 4.5.

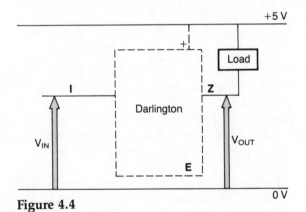

Figure 4.4

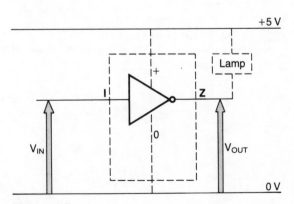

Figure 4.5

This has already been used in chapter 3 to represent a Darlington. This symbol really shows only what the circuit does and says nothing about the components which make it up. (The supply connections shown as two dotted lines are usually omitted from circuit diagrams. They are needed in practice to make the system work.)

A **load** is needed to make the circuit work properly e.g. a lamp between the Darlington output (Z) and the positive supply.

Take care not to confuse the state of the lamp with the output state of the system. It seems to be the wrong way round.

The lamp is **on** when the output voltage is **low**.

The lamp **off** when the output voltage is **high**.

Relay as a NOT gate

A relay system can be arranged to act as a NOT gate. Can you work out whether you need to use the NO or NC connection in fig 4.6? When you are ready for an answer, read on.

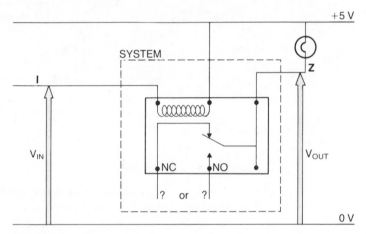

Figure 4.6

As shown, the input I is not connected. So, no current flows through the coil. This means the I is at high voltage. As we want an inverter, Z must be at low voltage. This can be done by connecting the normally closed (NC) contact to earth. (The lamp will then be on. Note that we are interested in the output voltage level – not whether the lamp is on or off). If I is earthed. The coil is activated and the NC link with earth is broken. This puts Z at high voltage. So we now have the inversion, low at I gives high at Z.

Relays are not generally used as logic systems as they require a significant current to activate the coil. Usually solid state systems are used which require a very small input current to make them work.

Two input logic gates

Now we will look at systems which have more than one input. One input will be called 'A' and the other 'B'. Both of them control the output, 'Z'.

The AND gate

Consider an example.
You can buy a snack if the shop is open AND you have enough money. We can represent this in a truth table. To buy the meal, both conditions have to be met. This is a straightforward truth statement which has two inputs.

Input A	Input B	Output Z
shop open?	enough money?	buy meal?
0	0	0
0	1	0
1	0	0
1	1	1

0=no 1=yes

An electric model of an AND gate would have two inputs (A and B). When both inputs are on (i.e. at high voltage) the output Z would be **on** (i.e. at high voltage), see fig 4.7. Unfortunately there is no simple way of building an AND gate from transistors and relays.
The Boolean symbol for AND is a full stop. So Z = A.B means Z is 1 if A is 1 AND B is 1.

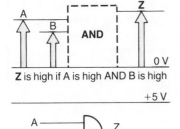

+5 V

Z is high if A is high AND B is high

+5 V

logic symbol for an AND gate

Figure 4.7

The OR gate

Let us start by looking at a truth example.
A house will have a beautiful garden if the householder is a keen gardener (A) OR can afford to employ a gardener (B). If one (or more) of the conditions is met then the garden will be beautiful. The **truth table** will be:

Input A	Input B	Output Z
keen gardener?	gardener employed?	beautiful garden?
0	0	0
0	1	1
1	0	1
1	1	1

0=false 1=true

This can be modelled electrically. Activity 4.1 is intended to let you work out how a relay could act as an OR gate. The logic symbol for an OR gate is shown in fig 4.8.
The Boolean algebra symbol for OR is '+', so Z = A + B means Z is 1 if A is 1 OR B is 1.

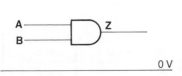

+5 V

0 V

Figure 4.8

The NOR gate

This is another gate with two inputs. The NOR gate is an abbreviation for 'NOT OR'. It is the opposite of OR, an inversion of OR. If we go back to the garden example, the NOR relation would be when the garden is NOT beautiful. It would be achieved when the householder is not a keen gardener and does not employ a gardener. The truth table would be:

Input A	Input B	Output Z
keen gardener?	gardener employed?	garden NOT beautiful?
0	0	1
0	1	0
1	0	0
1	1	0

0=false 1=true

The NOR gate can be built from a transistor with two inputs.

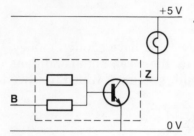

Figure 4.9

Fig 4.9 shows a circuit diagram for a transistor acting as a NOR gate. The two inputs are indicated by A and B and the output by Z.

Activity 4.1

A relay as an OR gate

Look at the 5 V relay connected as shown in fig 4.10. Assume that the input voltage is low unless connected to the +ve voltage supply line.

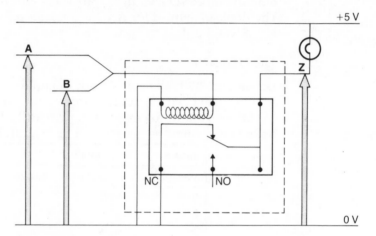

Figure 4.10

- What is the logic pattern?
- Can you complete the table below?

Input A		Input B		Output Z		Lamp
voltage	logic	voltage	logic	voltage	logic	on/off
low (not connected)	0	low (not connected)	0			
low (not connected)	0	high	1			
high	1	low (not connected)	0			
high	1	high	1			

- Can you explain how you reached your conclusions?
  The answers are given on page 71.

Activity 4.2

A transistor an a NOR gate

Consider a transistor which has two inputs A and B as shown in fig 4.11. This is a NOR gate.

- Can you work out what should go into the empty spaces in the table below?

Input A		Input B		Output Z		Lamp
voltage	*logic*	*voltage*	*logic*	*voltage*	*logic*	*on/off*
low	0	low	0			
low	0	high	1			
high	1	low	0			
high	1	high	1			

A NOR gate is a NOT OR.

- Can you see how the NOR and OR are related?

- Can you explain how you reached your conclusions?
  The answers are given on page 72.

Inverting a NOR gate to make an OR gate

You have seen how a transistor with two inputs makes a NOR gate. You know that a single input transistor acts as an inverter. If the output from the NOR gate is fed into an inverter, the final signal is NOT NOR. NOT NOR turns out to be the same as OR. The combination could be built and tested. The circuit is shown in fig 4.11 and the logic symbol in fig 4.12.

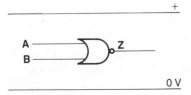

Figure 4.12

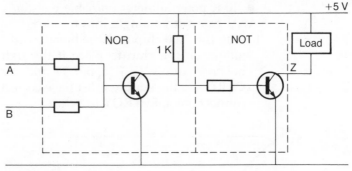

Figure 4.11

The remainder of this chapter explores how to use logic gates in a chip. The next type of gate to be studied will be the NAND gate (NOT AND). Then other types of gates will be investigated, using combinations of NAND gates.

What is a NAND gate circuit?

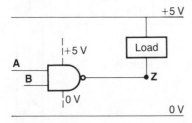

Figure 4.14

The symbol for a single NAND gate is shown in fig 4.13 with two inputs A and B and one output Z. The gate needs to be connected to the positive supply line (+5 V) and to earth (0 V). These connections are shown as dotted lines in the figure. These connections are needed to make the circuit work but they are usually left out of circuit diagrams to simplify the drawing.

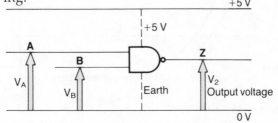

Figure 4.13

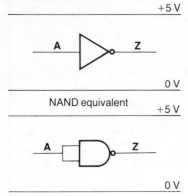

NAND equivalent

+5 V

0 V

+5 V

0 V

Figure 4.15

The gate can control a 'load' such as a small lamp connected between the output and the positive line, as shown in fig 4.14. A NAND gate with only one input acts as an INVERTER. That is a 0 at the input causes a 1 at the output, and an input of 1 gives an output of 0. Here the NAND gate is acting as a NOT gate. In other words the output is not what the input is. The symbol for a NOT gate is given in fig 4.15; together with the NAND gate equivalent.

If the output from a NAND is inverted, the whole combination becomes an AND gate. This is probably beginning to sound very muddled and complicated. Its best to try it in practice to see how this works.

Activity 4.3

Using NAND gates

The aim of this activity is to give you practical experience of logic gates and what they can do. We will use NAND gates contained in a chip. You need:

- 1 chip 7400 (two-input NAND gates)
- 1 chip 7410 (three-input NAND gates)
- 5 V dc supply or 4.5 V battery
- breadboard
- connecting wires
- voltmeter (5 V)
- led (light-emitting diode) with 470 R series resistor as a voltage indicator
- 1 K resistor
- 10 K potentiometer (variable resistor)

NAND gate with a **single** input.

1 Plug the 7400 chip into the breadboard as shown (fig 4.16). Use the indent on the chip to place it the right way round. Connect the positive supply (V_c) to pin 14 and earth (GND) to pin 7. **TAKE CARE** . . . the supply must have correct polarity. (Reversed supply connections **DESTROY** the chip.)

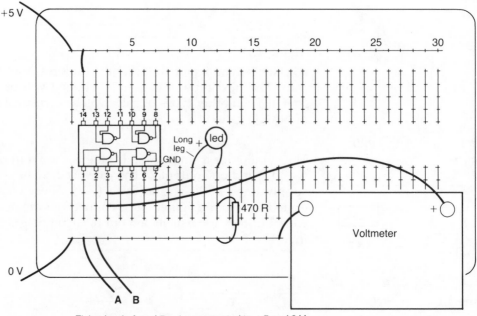

Flying leads A and B to be connected to +5 and 0 V

Figure 4.16

Activity 4.3 continued

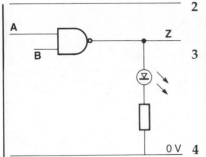

Figure 4.17

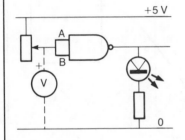

Figure 4.18

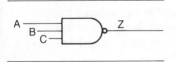

Figure 4.19

2 Select one of the gates for investigation. Connect the led with a 470 R resistor in series to show the voltage level at the output (fig 4.17). Note that the **led is not a load**. It replaces a voltmeter.

3 When using an led note two points;
(i)   you need a resistor about 470 R in series to limit the current,
(ii) the led, being a diode, carries current only one way.
So, you have to connect it the right way round. One leg is usually longer than the other. The long leg is connected to positive. The led will be **on** when the output voltage (Z) is high.

4 Start by linking the two inputs A and B together. This forms a logic gate with a single input. Now connect (A with B) to earth. Check that the output is HIGH (led on) when the input is LOW. If possible, check this with a voltmeter.

5 Take the input (A with B) to high voltage.
• What happens to the output voltage?
• Complete the truth table (low=0, high=1) for a 'one input' NAND gate.

Input	Output	Indicator lamp
A with B	Z	on/off
0		
1		

6 What happens when A with B is unconnected? Is the led on? It's often said that 'unconnected inputs float high'? Would you agree in this case?

7 Connect the potentiometer to give a variable voltage between 0 and 5 V. Use it as an input to the gate keeping A with B (fig 4.18). Then use a voltmeter to find the critical voltage which switches the gate. Is it 0.6 V like a single transistor or 1.4 V like a Darlington?

8 NAND gate with **two** inputs.
Now use inputs A and B separately. This gives you a NAND gate with two inputs.
• Then complete the table to show how the logic works.

Input	Input	Output
A	B	Z
0	0	
0	1	
1	0	
1	1	

Look at the output. It is supposed to be 'NOT' AND. (NAND means 'NOT' AND.) You would expect an AND gate to be on (i.e. gives an output of 1) when A is high AND B is high the output would be 0 for all other input combinations. The NOT is an inversion. So, invert these outputs and you have NOT AND (NAND.)
• Does this agree with your experimental values?

9 What happens when inputs are not connected to high or low voltage? Find out how the two-input NAND gate behaves when input A is left unconnected. Connect B to high and then low voltage. Is the result equivalent to A being high?

10 NAND gates with three inputs.
Gates can have more than two inputs (fig 4.19). Try using a 7410 chip which has NAND gates with three inputs (fig 4.20). Select one of the gates and see how it works. See fig 4.21 for help.
Call the inputs A, B and C.
Find out how the settings of A, B and C affect the output (Z). Can you complete the three-input NAND truth table below?

Activity 4.3 continued

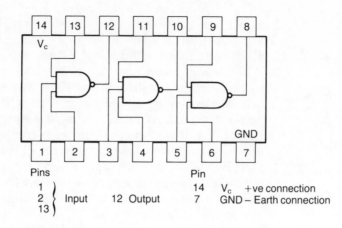

Figure 4.20

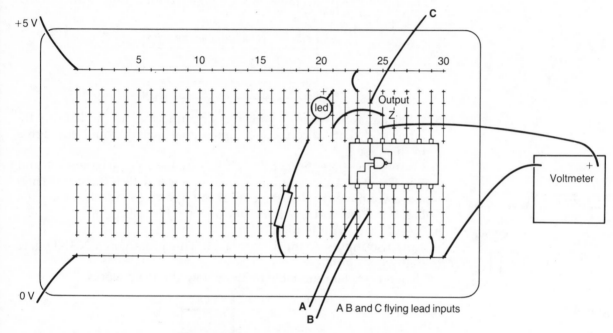

Figure 4.21

Inputs			Output
A	B	C	Z
0	0	0	
0	0	1	
0	1	0	
0	1	1	
1	0	0	
1	0	1	
1	1	0	
1	1	1	

- Can you sort out the pattern?
  It may be helpful to start by thinking about what would happen with a three input AND gate. A high output would be expected only when A and B and C are high. Then this output can be inverted to make a NOT AND.
- Does this agree with your results?

Activity 4.4

Making other gates by combining NAND gates

You can make up other logic gates by linking NAND gates together. This activity explores how to do it. Having done this, you will be able to use logic gates to solve some practical control problems.

1 Making one AND gate from two NAND gates.
The AND gate gives an output 1 when both inputs are 1.

A	B	Z
0	0	0
0	1	0
1	0	0
1	1	1

If A is 1 AND B is 1 then output Z is 1.
Otherwise, Z is 0.
This is the inverse of the output from a NAND gate.

2 Can you make one AND gate from two NAND gates and check that its operation is correct?
All you have to do is to take the output from one NAND gate and invert it. Remember that a single input NAND behaves as an inverter. Does fig 4.22 help?
Use the 7400 chip. Take the output from your first gate and make it the input to your second gate.
A possible breadboard layout is given in fig 4.23.

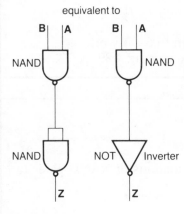

Figure 4.22

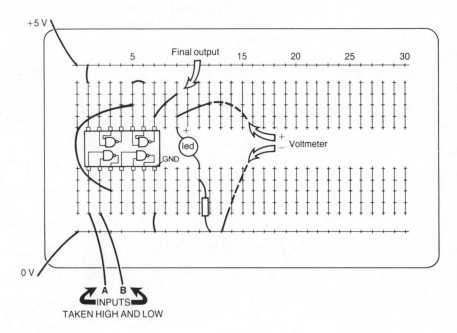

Figure 4.23

Activity 4.4 continued

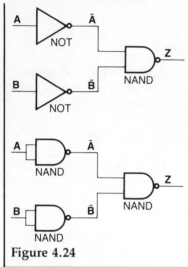

Figure 4.24

3 Making one OR gate from three NAND gates.
The OR gate gives an output 1 when input A is 1 or B is 1 or when A and B are both 1.

A	B	Z	
0	0	0	OR gate
0	1	1	
1	0	1	
1	1	1	

It's not easy to work out how to combine NAND gates to give the OR function. You need three gates.
You have to invert input A, invert input B and then feed these into a NAND gate (fig 4.24). (In Boolean notation 'NOT A' is represented by a bar above A ie $\bar{A}$.)
Try it using a 7400 chip to see if you can make it work.
If you need help with breadboard layout see fig 4.39, p. 72.

Activity 4.5

Solving practical problems using logic gates

This activity shows how you can use combinations of NAND gates to solve a practical problem.

Building logic units from NAND gates

You can combine NAND gates to give any logic relation. Fig 4.25 shows how NAND gates can be combined to give NOT, AND, OR and NOR. On this basis, given enough NAND gates you could build up any logic system you want.

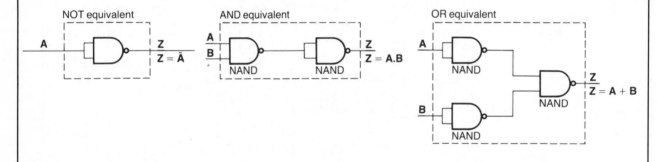

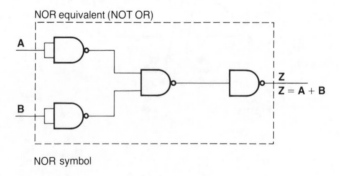

NOR symbol

Figure 4.25

Activity 4.5 continued

A method for solving practical problems

The problems can be solved in the following stages:-

(a) Write down the logic relation

(b) Draw a block plan using the logic functions AND, OR, NOT, etc.

(c) Convert this to a set of NAND gate equivalents.

(d) Look for simplifications. Two inversions are equivalent to doing nothing fig 4.26.

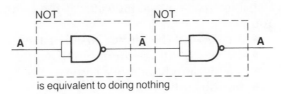

Figure 4.26

(e) Connect up and test.
   Remember that you need to connect a +5 V supply to run each chip.
   To see what all this means, follow through an example.

Build a logic system that will switch a light on when someone is nearby but which only works at night.

The signal showing that someone is close by could come from a pressure pad or perhaps an infra-red movement sensor. [person near = P]. A light sensor could give a signal when it is night [night = N]. For simplicity consider the input and output voltage levels. Ignore how they could be obtained and how the input might work the light!

You need:-
* 1 chip 7400 (two-input NAND gates)
* 5 V dc supply or 4.5 V battery
* breadboard
* connecting wires
* voltmeter (5 V)
* led (light-emitting diode) with 470 R series resistor as voltage indicator
* switch to represent pressure pad
* 10 K potentiometer (variable resistor)
* ldr

Following through the stages we have:

(a) Decide which logic relations are involved. In this case, the output [Z] is high if a person is near by [P=1] AND it is night [N=1]. So, an AND is required.
   (In Boolean notation this would be Z = P.N i.e Z is 1 if P is 1 AND N is 1.)

(b) The block plan using the AND logic function is given in fig 4.27.

(c) This is converted to a set of NAND gates in fig 4.28.

(d) We have no places where one inversion is followed by another, so no simplification can be done here.

(e) A breadboard layout for an AND gate has already been given in fig 4.23. You simply change inputs A and B for P and N.
   The sensors are not included but you ought to have ideas about how you could connect them up. Your theory should be based on the voltage divider.
   You would need to use the ideas of Chapters 2 and 3 to use the output Z to operate relays or solid state switches.
   The led used as a voltage indicator will be the quickest way to show that the circuit is working.

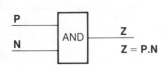

Figure 4.27

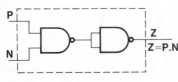

Figure 4.28

Activity 4.6

Some practical problems

These problems involve designing logic circuits. Build them with NAND chips. Test them by taking the inputs to high and low voltage. However, you should have some ideas about how the inputs could be sensed electronically and may even wish to go on and build them. Use a led as a voltage indicator at the output.

You need:

- 1 chip 7400 (two-input NAND gates)
- 1 chip 7410 (three-input NAND gates)
- 5 V dc supply or 4.5 V battery
- breadboard
- connecting wires
- voltmeter (5 V)
- led (light-emitting diode) with 470 R series resistor as voltage indicator

1 **The insomniac**

An insomniac doesn't want to be disturbed after dark and is asking for a door bell which does not work at night. A light sensor could be used to monitor when it is night-time.

The logic system gives positive output (which rings the bell) when these two conditions are met:

(a) the bell push is pressed

(b) it is NOT at night.

Use two inputs, one for bell [B] and one for night time [N]. There is no need to actually connect a bell, you can use an ldr as an indicator. Take the inputs high and low to give the conditions.

2 **The alarm**

An intruder alarm is needed which will work when:

(a) the system is switched on [O]

(b) it is night [N]

(c) an intruder is present [I]

Use an ldr to indicate the output.

3 **The washing line**

A housewife wants an automatic system which will bring her washing undercover (by pulling it indoors or putting up a large umbrella). It should do this when the following conditions are met:

(a) it is raining [R]

(b) it is night [N]

(c) there is no sun [S] and no wind [W]

The solutions to these problems are given on page 73.

TTL critical input voltage

The logic gate chips you have used so far are known as Transistor Transistor Logic (TTL). They do not have a precise critical input voltage, more a range of uncertainty.

What is certain is that:

2.4 to 5.5 V is high and

0 to 0.4 V is low.

The output from TTL chips is better able to **sink** current from a load rather than **source** current to it (fig 4.29).

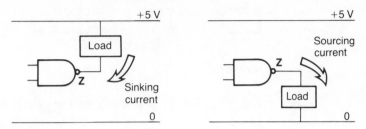

Figure 4.29

We have always placed any load between the positive supply and the system output. For example, with a transistor, the load current 'sinks' into the collector (see fig 4.2).

In a similar way, consider the logic gate output as a collector.

If you link this 'collector' to the +5 V supply through a resistor the voltage at Z will be high or low depending on the gate inputs (fig 4.30). A voltage divider has been formed between the resistor and the logic gate.

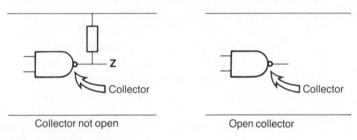

Figure 4.30

Some logic gates have the resistor included internally. Others do not. These are **open collector** chips. To control the output voltage in open collector chips a resistor or load must be added.

The 7400 and 7410 chips you have used are not open collector. They have an internal connection to the +5 V supply. That is why the output between gates can be connected without adding load resistors.

The NAND chip is built with each input connected internally to the positive supply via a large resistor. (However, it is considered good practice to link unused inputs to a definite voltage level. There is a small chance that some 'stray' voltages may upset the working.)

There is another family of chips called CMOS. They have a different switching range. See Chapter 9, page 152 for more details.

A small collection of gates will usually do only one job. A computer is built from a vast collection of logic gates together with an electronic timer. This makes it a flexible control system and one which we shall now go on to use.

Summary

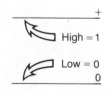

Figure 4.31

In a logic approach there are only two states.
The kind of state depends on the system eg:
1/0; high/low voltage; on/off; alive/dead; true/false (see fig 4.31)

Electronic systems which switch between two states can be treated as logic systems

Concentrate on the input and output voltage.

    voltage > critical level is logic 1
    voltage < critical level is logic 0

There are different logic gates eg:
NOT, AND, OR, NAND, NOR (fig 4.32)

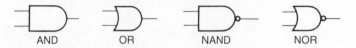

AND   OR   NAND   NOR

Figure 4.32

NOT

Figure 4.33

A NOT gate has only one input, the others have more. (fig 4.33)

NOT inverts the voltage. Practical examples are: transistor, Darlington, relay, NAND gate.

Figure 4.34

Relations can get NOTed by adding an inverter, see fig 4.34.

Any logic relation can be built up from a combination of NAND gates.

Unconnected inputs in TTL chips float high.

Consolidation questions

A warning sign needs to be automatically switched on at night OR at any other time by a manual over-ride switch.
    [Z] state of warning sign (Z=0 off, Z=1 on)
    [N] night (N=0 daytime, N=1 night)
    [S] Switch setting (S=0 off, S=1 on)
* The control circuit is to be worked by a 5 V supply?

1. Complete the truth table below showing what should happen.

Inputs		Output
N	S	Z
0	0	
0	1	
1	0	
1	1	

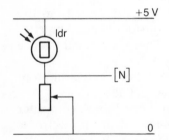

+5 V

ldr

[N]

0

Figure 4.35

2 An ldr will be used to report when it is night. The ldr has a high resistance in darkness and will be part of a voltage divider circuit. The voltage level [N] should be high at night and low during the day. This part of the circuit is shown in fig 4.35.
* Will it do the job?

3 Look at the logic diagram shown in fig 4.36.
You can buy OR gates in a chip. The 7432 chip has 4 OR gates (called a quadruple two-input OR). The pin connections are shown in fig 4.37.

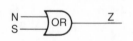

Figure 4.36

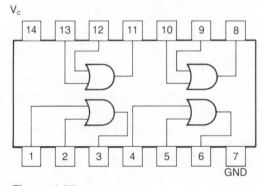

Figure 4.37

The circuit has been built up on breadboard using an OR chip as shown in fig 4.38.
It does not work.
- How many errors can you find?

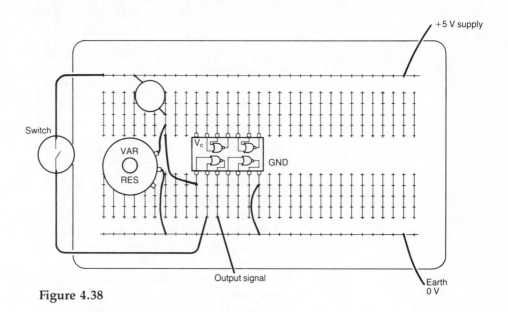

Figure 4.38

4 What circuit could be set up using only NAND gates? Would this have any advantages over using the ready made OR gates?

Solutions

Activity 4.1

The table for the OR gate is completed below.

Input A		Input B		Output Z		Lamp
voltage	logic	voltage	logic	voltage	logic	on/off
low (not connected)	0	low (not connected)	0	low	0	ON
low (not connected)	0	high	1	high	1	OFF
high	1	low (not connected)	0	high	1	OFF
high	1	high	1	high	1	OFF

A simplified logic table looks like:

Input A	Input B	Output Z
0	0	0
0	1	1
1	0	1
1	1	1

If your table is not the same, check that you have noticed that the NC connection is used. When inputs A and B are not connected no current can flow through the coil. However if inputs A and B are at low voltage the output Z is connected to earth-through NC, so Z will be at low voltage. (The lamp will be on). When either of the inputs A and B, or both of them, are at high voltage the coil is active and Z will also be at high voltage, as it is no longer linked to earth. (The lamp is off).

Activity 4.2

The NOR gate table should be:

Input A		Input B		Output Z		Lamp
voltage	logic	voltage	logic	voltage	logic	on/off
low	0	low	0	high	1	OFF
low	0	high	1	low	0	ON
high	1	low	0	low	0	ON
high	1	high	1	low	0	ON

which simplifies to:

Input A	Input B	Output Z
0	0	1
0	1	0
1	0	0
1	1	0

In other words you only get a high voltage at output (Z) when inputs A and B are **both** at low voltage.

Any high voltage at the base of the transistor will make it active and take the voltage at Z down to low. It does not matter whether the voltage is supplied at either A or B or both.

Notice that the NOR gate output is the reverse of the OR gate.
Remember that NOR means 'NOT OR'. This is the inverse of the OR function. The logic symbol is shown in fig 4.12. In logic diagrams, the 'o' in the output line means inverse or NOT. Compare this with the logic symbol for OR – fig 4.8, here there is no 'o' in the output (Z) line.

Activity 4.4

See fig 4.39.

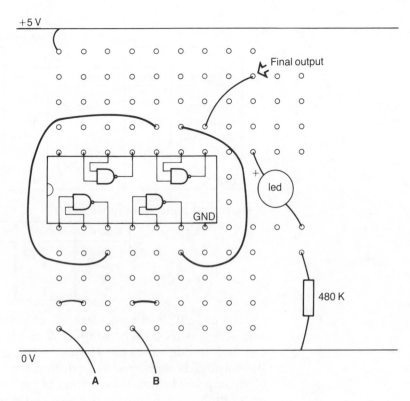

Figure 4.39

Activity 4.6

The following points are limited to the first three stages of a solution. i.e.

(a) logic relation
(b) bock plan of logic functions
(c) NAND equivalents

1 The insomniac

(a) The output (Z) is high if the bell is pushed (B =high) AND it is NOT night ($\overline{N}$ =high).

$Z = B \cdot \overline{N}$

(b) See fig 4.40

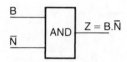

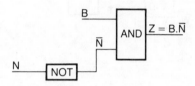

Figure 4.40

(c) See fig 4.41

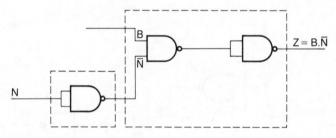

Figure 4.41

2 The alarm

(a) The output (Z) is high if the system is switched on (S =high) AND it is night (N =high) AND an intruder is present (I =high)

$Z = S \cdot N \cdot I$

(b) This needs a three-input gate fig 4.42

(c) See fig 4.43

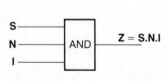

Figure 4.42

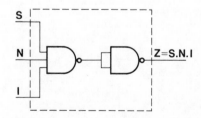

Figure 4.43

3 The washing line

(a) The output (Z) is high which brings the washing undercover if it is raining (R = high) OR it is night (N =high) OR there is no sun (S) AND no wind ($\overline{W}$)

$$Z = R + N + \overline{S} \cdot \overline{W}$$

(b) See fig 4.44

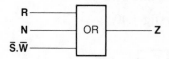

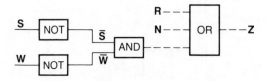

Figure 4.44

(c) See fig 4.45.

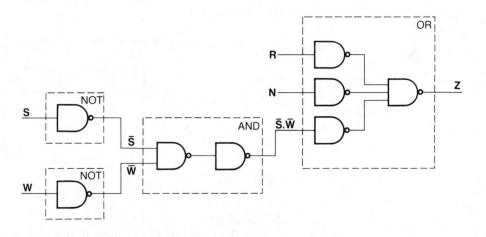

Figure 4.45

5 Linking with a BBC computer – outputs from the user port

Introduction

Up to now we have been looking at some general principles of electronics. We are now in a position to link circuits to a computer and use it for control. The rest of this book is concerned with control using a computer. The BBC computer has two ports located underneath, the **user port** and the **printer port** where voltage signals can be obtained for control (fig 5.1).

In this chapter we will see how to make a computer switch lights and motors on and off. To do this some kind of **buffer** between your circuits and the computer will be needed. The buffer gives some protection against misconnections. It also 'boosts' the power of computer signals. Computer data signals do not supply enough power to work lamps and motors. The signals are used to control other sources of power. Sometimes the power source is a low voltage supply from the computer. In other cases it is an external supply.

There are a number of commercial buffers which link to the computer user port and printer ports. However, you can build your own at minimum cost. Eventually, this should give you a fuller understanding of how the systems work. The first part of the chapter gives construction details for three kinds of buffer board.

Three kinds of buffer board

Three kinds of buffer board are described.
1   User port demonstration board
2   User port, four-input and four-output board
3   Printer port, output board only
Of these, the user port four-input and four-output board is likely to be the most useful and the one I suggest that you build. The demonstration board is useful only as an introduction for showing how the user port works. The printer port board is likely to be needed at a later stage when more control lines are needed. Further details of these boards follow:

User port demonstration board

This is not really a buffer at all. It simply makes a direct link to the user port connections. It is only suitable for an initial investigation of how the user port works and should not be used for practical applications. It is only really worth building if this is to be done a number of times.

User port, four-input and four-output board

This will be referred to as the **Marjon buffer board**. It has four output and four input lines. It gives some protection to the computer and uses the +5 V computer supply. A printed circuit board (pcb) can be purchased, making it easy to construct.

Printer port, outputs only

I call this the **Chelt-out board**. It uses the eight output lines from the printer port. It is built on stripboard and useful when you want more than the four output lines available on the Marjon board.

Boards 2 and 3 cost around £10 each and the demonstration board rather less. The socket connections for the BBC computer user port are shown in fig 5.1. We are not using the control bits (CB1 and CB2) at this stage.

BBC USER PORT

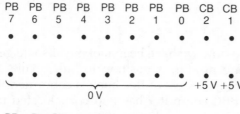

Socket connections as seen from outside the computer

PB = Port Bit
CB = Control Bit – not used
0 V = Earth

Figure 5.1

Building buffer boards

This section gives details of how to build the three types of buffer board. As the connections are permanent the components are soldered.

Some general practical advice

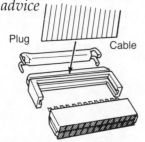

Plug
Cable

Figure 5.2

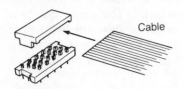

Cable

Figure 5.3

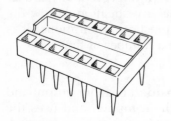

Figure 5.4

Before embarking on details about the individual boards there are some general points worth noting.

1 The BBC computer has socket connections for the user port and printer ports, underneath the machine. These need special plugs which can be easily connected to ribbon cable. Basically, the ribbon cable is threaded into the plug and the parts carefully but firmly squeezed together in a vice (fig 5.2). Take special care to get the plug the right way round by looking at the diagrams. The other end of the ribbon cable is linked to a connector which is soldered to the board (fig 5.3) Do not be tempted to save money by trying to solder connections. Not only is it very tedious, but the connections will fall apart quickly.

2 When using chips, it is good practice to use a chip socket (fig 5.4). This will avoid any danger of damaging the chip with heat from the soldering iron and allow easy replacement.

3 A fine tipped soldering iron is advised. Even so, at some stage you will accidentally bridge two lines. A solder 'sucker' helps no end in removing excess solder (fig 5.5).

4 The best way of soldering a component to the board is to bring the tip of the soldering iron flat against the post or wire. At the same time touch the metal strip, then melt some solder at the tip of the soldering iron, which will flow over and make a good connection (fig 5.6).

De-soldering tool

RS 544-516 (£7)

Figure 5.5

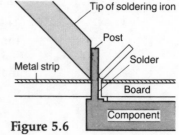

Tip of soldering iron
Post
Solder
Metal strip
Board
Component

Figure 5.6

5   Use single-strand insulated wire to make connections between components. It is easier to solder than multistrand. Only use multistrand connecting wire if it has to be flexible and is going to be bent often.

6   Break the continuous strip of copper on a stripboard using a small drill bit which can be twisted by hand or you can buy a special stripboard track cutter (RS543–535).

User port demonstration board – direct connections

This board makes direct connection to the user port terminals (fig 5.7).

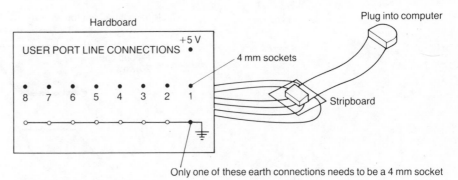

Figure 5.7

To make a user port demonstration board you need:
- 0.5 m 20-way ribbon cable (RS360–122)
- 1 user port plug 20-way (RS467–289)
- 4 cm × 4 cm approx stripboard, 0.25 mm spaced holes (RS433–826)
- 1 ribbon cable connector to stripboard (RS468–147)
- 10 4 mm sockets (RS444–618)
- connecting wire (multistrand) 1 m lengths
- 30 cm × 40 cm approx hardboard

You also need:
- soldering iron (20 W) with fine tip, solder (with resin core)
- scissors, wire strippers and selection of drill bits

1   Mark out and drill holes in the hardboard panel to receive the 4 mm sockets. Fig 5.7 shows a possible layout. You only need one 'earth' socket.

2   Solder the ribbon cable connector socket to the stripboard (fig 5.8).

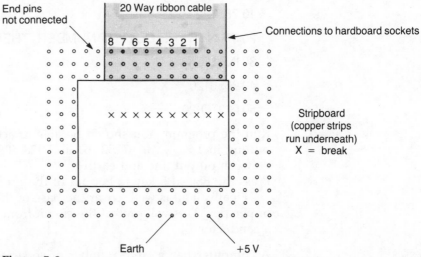

Figure 5.8

Make 10 breaks in the copper strip (marked x in fig 5.8) so that the pins are not connected. You can do this using a drill bit.

3   Insert the cable, taking care to leave the end pins unconnected as shown in fig 5.8. Use a wood block to protect the exposed pins then squeeze the cover, wires and socket together in a vice.

4   Connect the plug to the other end of the cable. Take special care here. The cable is folded over the top of the plug, but only after the plug has been squeezed together. See fig 5.9. (Some plugs have a **notch** allowing connection to the computer only one way round. If yours has a notch it should be at the top.)

5   Finally, solder connections between the stripboard and the 4 mm sockets (figs 5.7 and 5.8).

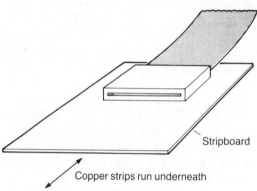

Figure 5.9

Testing the demonstration board

Start with the computer newly switched on, Connect the plug to the user port underneath the computer. (If there is a marked reaction from the computer, e.g. flashing screen and noise. Switch off quickly – there is something wrong. Check your connections.) Check the +5 V using a voltmeter between +5 V and earth.

Try the following program:

(Press the RETURN key at the end of each line when typing it in.)

```
10 ?65122 = 255

20 PRINT"TYPE OUTPUT NUMBER, THEN PRESS RETURN"

30 INPUT X

40 ?656120 = X

50 GOTO 20
```

Run the program. You should be able to activate each output in turn by putting in 1, 2, 4, 8, 16, 32, 64 and 128. Test by connecting a voltmeter between output line and earth.

Press the ESCAPE key to get out of the program.

Finally, if all is well, cover the base of the stripboard with card, wood or perspex. This will protect the circuit from shorting out if it is placed on a conductor.

Addresses

A computer has a large number of separate memory locations. Each of these locations has an individual number or address. The computer can use these numbers, the address of the location, to select the data contained there. The terms register and memory location are alternative names for the address.

For the BBC computer the address numbered 65122 has been made the Data Direction Register. This register or address holds information about whether data is passing in or out of the 8 user port lines. Before using address 65122 the voltage level on each line is 0.8 V. After making a line into output the voltage falls to zero. Each of the 8 lines is controlled by a number in turn by 1, 2, 4, 8, 16, 32, 64, 128. To switch on line one you need to type in ?65122 = 1

To switch on more than one line at a time you need to add the **'bit' values** of the lines together. So to switch on all the 8 lines ?65122 = 255 has to be typed in. The figure 255 is the sum of 1+2+4+8+16+32+64+128. This is the number you typed in for the first line of the program used to test the demonstration board.

?65122 = 255 means let the contents of register 65122 be 255

To control the voltage settings of the output lines you need to use another address, this is 65120. Again each line is controlled in the same way, e.g. line 4 by typing in ?65120 = 8 and to control more than one line the 'bit' values of those lines are added up.

Port Bits

The port bits (labelled PB on fig 5.1) are numbered 0, 1, 2, 3, 4, 5, 6, 7 and are represented by the abbreviation PB, e.g. PB0, PB1, etc. Although the first port bit is called 0 it is controlled by the number 1 is address 65120. Computer designers call the first thing in a series of things **zero**. This is similar to what we do when counting the floors in a building. If you want a number for the ground floor it would be 0, the next floor up is the first floor.

Marjon user port buffer board

Building the Marjon Buffer board
This type of port buffer board is highly recommended and is very useful for practical projects. It has four putput and four input lines. The name Marjon is derived from the College of St Mark and St John, Plymouth, where it was designed originally. Pcb's can be obtained from the College for about £3.
You need:
- I/O pcb (input/output printed circuit board)
- 2 10 nF capacitors (optional) (RS 124–140)
- 2 integrated circuit NAND chips
  1 74LS00 (RS 307–480)
  1 7400 (RS 305–490)
- 2 470 R resistors (RS 131–211) (for red and green LEDs)
- 2 220 R resistors (RS 131–176) (for yellow LEDs)
- 4 3 mm LEDs
  1 red, (RS 588–291)
  2 yellow (RS 588–314)
  1 green (RS 588–308)
- 2 14 pin dual in line (DIL) chip sockets (RS 402–765)
- 0.5 m 20-way ribbon cable (RS 360–122) (Farnell will supply short sections of ribbon cable. So will Maplin*, with the benefit of a plug already fitted)
- 1 20-way IDC connector (RS 467–289)
- 1 20-way IDC to pcb connector (RS 468–147)
- terminal block 10-way 4 mm barrel or other form of connections (RS 423–554)
- single strand connecting wire

For the construction you also need:
- soldering iron (20 W) with fine tip, solder (with resin core), cutting pliers or scissors, wire strippers.

see Appendix page 197 for the addresses of these suppliers.

1 Push the ends of the components through the holes in the pcb, see fig 5.10. The conducting tracks are on the underside of the board.

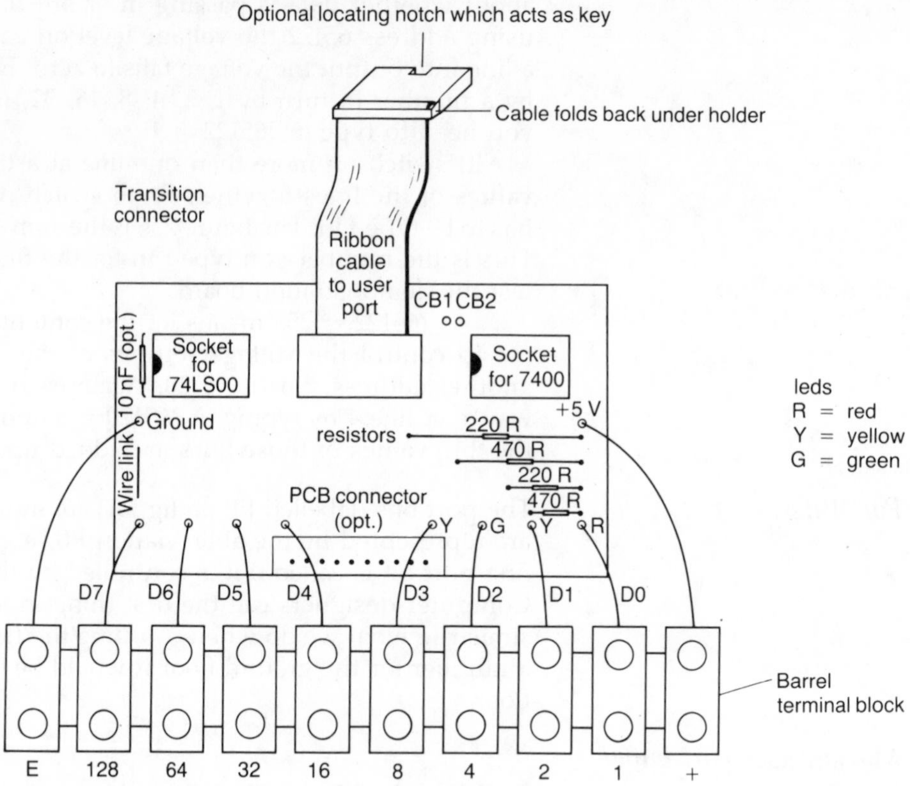

Figure 5.10 components/labels: Optional locating notch which acts as key; Cable folds back under holder; Transition connector; Ribbon cable to user port; CB1 CB2; Socket for 74LS00; Socket for 7400; Wire link 10 nF (opt.); Ground; resistors; 220 R; 470 R; 220 R; 470 R; +5 V; leds R = red, Y = yellow, G = green; PCB connector (opt.); Y G Y R; D7 D6 D5 D4 D3 D2 D1 D0; Barrel terminal block; E 128 64 32 16 8 4 2 1 +

Figure 5.10

2 Fit the chip sockets, not the chips.
3 Leds must be connected the right way round. Two kinds exist. One has a flat over the −ve connection. When there is no flat place, the shorter leg is −ve. See fig 5.11. The negative connection goes towards the bottom end of the board. Each colour of the LED needs its own value resistor in series to give the right brightness.
4 Solder the ends, making sure that solder does not flow across onto other tracks. Snip off excess wire after soldering.
5 Ribbon cable connections.
First, fix the ribbon cable to the connector which is already soldered to the board. See fig 5.3. Place it in a vice with a small wood block behind the pins to prevent damage as you tighten the vice. Gently squeeze the lid into place.

Then, connect the computer plug. Take special care to get it the right way round. This may be difficult because the cable folds back over the top of the plug after the cable has been connected. (Some plugs have a locating notch. This should end up on top see fig 5.10.) Double check before you squeeze the plug in a vice (see figs 5.12 and 5.13).

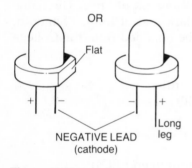

OR
Flat
+ −   − +
NEGATIVE LEAD (cathode)
Long leg

Figure 5.11

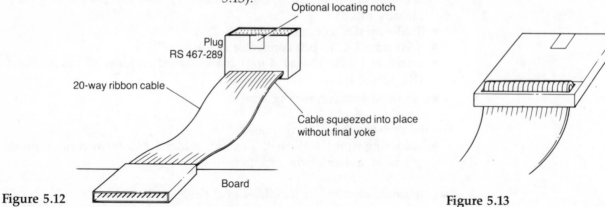

Figure 5.12 labels: Optional locating notch; Plug RS 467-289; 20-way ribbon cable; Cable squeezed into place without final yoke; Board

Figure 5.12

Figure 5.13

6   If barrel terminal blocks are used to make contact with the outside world they should be fixed on the board. The suggested method is to make a saw cut along the top edge and slot them into the board. Make the connections, then fix with a glue gun.

7   Chips have a small notch at one end. They **must** be connected the right way round. Check with the diagram (fig 5.10). Mark the notch position on the board.

8   When you have finished construction, check that you have plugged in the chips correctly and test.

   a Start with the computer newly switched on.

   b Plug the board into the user port. (If there is a marked reaction from the computer, such as a flashing screen or noise . . Switch off quickly. There is something wrong. Check your connections and soldering.)

   c All the leds should come on. If they do not try connecting the plug the other way round.

9   Sample test program:
   (Remember to press RETURN at the end of each line when writing in the program)

```
10 ?65122 = 15
20 PRINT"TYPE IN THE OUTPUT NUMBER, THEN PRESS
   RETURN"
30 INPUT X
40 ?65120 = X
50 GOTO 20
```

   On running the program, make the output number (X) = 1, 2, 4 and 8 in turn. The leds should light in response.

10   Testing inputs
   The Marjon board also can take in information. Type NEW followed by RETURN and enter the following program:

```
10 ?65122 = 15
20 print ?65120
30 GOTO 20
```

   On running the prgram you should find a number scrolling up the screen. Connecting the earth to each one of the input lines in turn should change the number to 16, then 32, then 64 and finally to 128.
   Escape will get you out of the program.

11   Finally, if all is well, cover the base of the stripboard with card, wood or perspex. This stops shorting out if the stripboard is accidentally placed on a conductor.

Chelt-out, eight-line output using printer port

The printer port has eight-output lines which are normally used to control a printer. The port has no +5 V supply to run chips or loads and only provides data signals. So, an external low voltage supply will be required. In this output buffer board, the output data is used to run LED indicator lamps and activate Darlingtons. The leds and Darlingtons are in chips. (The chips are called **dual in line** (DIL). In practice this means that they fit into stripboard.)

The circuit is built on stripboard. Connections to the outside are made through stripboard-socket connectors. The layout is designed to require minimum soldering (fig 5.14).

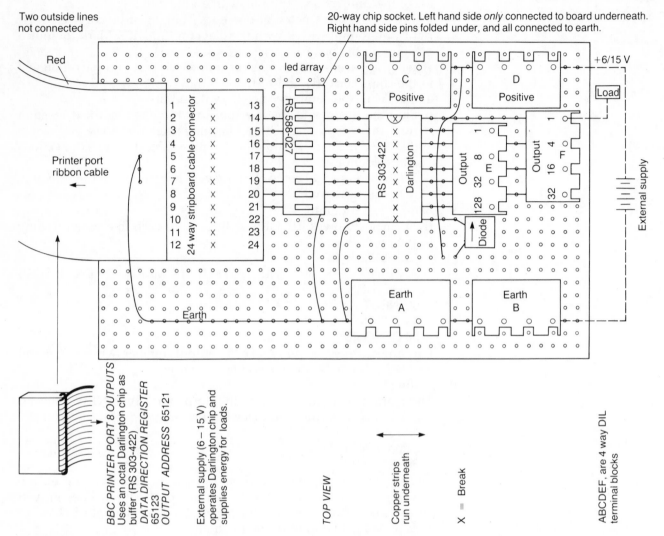

Figure 5.14

You will need:
- 9 cm × 9 cm approx stripboard 2.5 mm (RS 433–826)
- 1 Octal Darlington chip as buffer (RS 303–422)
- 1 18-way chip socket (RS 402–204)
- 1 20-way chip socket (RS 402–210)
- 1 26-way cable plug (RS 467–295)
- 1 26-line ribbon cable (0.5 m) (RS 360–150) (short lengths from Farnell or Maplin)
- 1 24 pin DIL stripboard cable connector (RS 468–276)
- 1 led array (RS 588–027)
- 6 4-way DIL terminal blocks (Farnell 146–258) (Barrell terminal blocks can be substituted)
- 1 Power diode (Farnell BY 249–300)

Construction notes

1 Section the stripboard with the copper strips running lengthways. Solder in the 24 pin cable connector (fig 5.14).
2 Find the 20-way socket for the led array. Fold one set of legs under the socket and solder a connection between them which can be taken to earth. The other set of legs is soldered to the stripboard. This is not an ideal arrangement but it does simplify the stripboard connections (fig 5.14).

3   Solder in the 18-way socket for the Darlington.

4   Break the copper strips at the places marked **X** on the figure (22 breaks).

5   Fix the ribbon cable on to the 24-way socket on the board. Note that two of the ribbon cable lines are not connected and should be cut short. Place the cable in position, put a small piece of wood under the soldered legs, and gently squeeze the lid onto the socket, using a vice.

6   Fit the plug to the ribbon cable taking care to get it the right way round. Close the plug in a vice.

7   Solder in the terminal blocks and power diode. The power diode gives protection if the external low voltage supply is connected the wrong way round.

8   Plug in the led array and Darlington chips. Make sure they are the right way round. Only 8 of the leds are used.

9   Check carefully that your connections are correct, that the copper strips have been broken at the points marked with an 'X' on the figure and no rails are accidentally connected by solder. Are the chips plugged in the right way round?

10 Now test the board. Start with the computer newly switched on. Plug into the printer port.
    Sample test program:
```
10 ?65123 = 255
20 PRINT"TYPE IN THE OUTPUT NUMBER AND PRESS RETURN"
30 INPUT X
40 ?65121 = X
50 GOTO 20
```
    On running the program, make the number = 1, 2, 4, 8, 16, 32, 64, 128 to control each output line in turn. The leds should light up in response. Connect an external 5 V dc supply. Connect a 6 V lamp as a load (fig 5.14). Check that this works at each output.

11 Finally, after testing, cover the copper tracks with card, wood or perspex to prevent shorting between them.

Practical Introduction to the User port

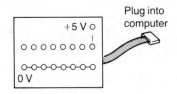

Figure 5.15

If you have one to hand, the demonstration board (fig 5.15) is useful for showing how the user port works.
You can show:

1   The outputs can only be controlled by the computer after setting the DATA DIRECTION REGISTER. This is address 65122. Putting 255 into address 65122 makes all lines outputs.

2   Before using address 65122, the voltage level on each output line is 0.8 V. After making a line act as output, its voltage level falls to zero.

3   The working address is 65120. When numbers are put into this address (e.g. 1, 2, 4, 8) the voltage level of the associated output line changes.

4   The voltage is 0 if the line is off and around 2.5 V if it is on. However, all of this will be much more meaningful if you try it out in practice. Activity 5.1 can only be done if you have a demonstration board to hand and is therefore optional. If you do not have one, move onto Activity 5.2 which covers much the same ground.

Activity 5.1 (optional)

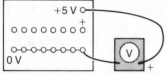

Figure 5.16

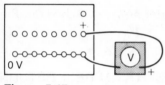

Figure 5.17

Using the Demonstration board
This activity shows how you can change the voltage levels on the output lines by writing instructions into the computer. Later you will use these voltage levels to control lamps and motors.
You need:
- demonstration board fig 5.15 (*see page 77 for construction details*)
- 0–5 V voltmeter and connecting leads.

Push the plug gently into the user port. use the voltmeter to check that 5 V line is active when the computer is switched on (fig 5.16) (If the voltmeter does not work, reverse the plug into the computer).

You cannot switch the +5 V on and off under computer control. So far, the computer is providing a voltage difference – just like a battery (at £400, a rather expensive battery!).

Connect the voltmeter between the first output line (PB0) and earth (fig 5.17).

You can change the voltage on this line by writing to addresses in the computer. Initially, the voltmeter should read about 0.8 V.

The first step is to put 255 into address 65122. Do this by typing:
LET ?65122 = 255 (followed by RETURN)
Did you notice the voltmeter change when you pressed 'RETURN'? To control the output voltage you need to use another address – 65120.

To change the state of the **first line** (port bit 0) write
LET ?65120 = 1
followed by 'RETURN'
The voltmeter should read a voltage well in excess of 0.8 V and the line is said to be ON.
See what happens when you type
LET ?65120 = 0 (RETURN)
Now move the voltmeter connection to the second line.
So, we are now using the **second line** (which is called port bit **1**). What number in address 65120 will switch it on? Try 2. i.e. write
LET ?65120 = 2 (RETURN)
You should now be able to control the first two lines.
Move the voltmeter onto the third line (PB2).
- What number will switch this on?
- What number would switch all eight lines on?

Summary
You should now know that:
1 The data direction register is 65122.
2 To put a number into an address you use a ? in front of the address. For example,
LET ?65122 = 15 puts 15 into address 65122
? means 'the contents of address . . .
3 The number put into the Data Direction Register determines which lines are to be outputs.
4 To control voltage levels on the output lines, you write to a working address (65120). Each line is associated with a particular '**bit**' number, e.g. 1, 2, 4, etc. For example, ?65120 = 4 would raise the voltage level on the third line.

Activity 5.2

Output from the user port (Marjon buffer board)
This activity explores how to control the user port output lines.
Use the indicator lamps to show what is happening.
You need:
  • Marjon board (fig 5.10)
Begin with no program in the computer. (Type NEW followed by RETURN or switch off and on.)
Connect the buffer board to the use port underneath the computer. Gently locate the plug in the right pins and then push it firmly home. take care not to bend any pins. The four light-emitting diodes (leds) should light up. (If they do not, connect the plug the other way round.)

The voltage levels suoplied by the computer cannot be used for driving any significant load. They can light the indicator lamps (leds) and a small wattage lamp (6 V 0.06 A).

Check that you can identify the following 10 connections (fig 5.18)
  i +5 V – the computer gives a +5 V supply to work chips and drive small loads.
  ii 0 V – earth reference line
  iii 8 data lines.

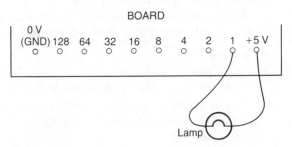

Figure 5.18

Controlling the output lines
  1 The first step is to put 15 into address 65122. This informs the computer that lines 1, 2, 4, 8 are outputs. Do this by typing
      LET ?65122 = 15 (then press RETURN)
      The four leds should go off.
  2 To change the setting of the first output line type
      LET ?65120 = 1 (followed by RETURN)
      This means 'LET the contents of register 65120 = 1' (Remember that Address 65120 controls the voltage setting on the output lines.)
      Does the indicator lamp come on?
      Now put 0 into address 65120.
      • Does the lamp switch off?
      To control the second line, set the contents of address 65120 to 2. Type
      LET ?65120 = 2 (followed by RETURN)
      Switch it off by setting the contents of 65120 to zero.
  4 How do you control the next line?
  5 How do you switch the first and third lines on? Try 5.
  6 How do you switch them all on?
This was the reason why we put 15 into the Data Direction Register (65122). It is the sum of 1 + 2 + 4 + 8 and makes the first four lines outputs. The other lines are inputs and we will come to that later.

So, now you should be able to control the first four output lines as you wish. Check that you can do so.

Activity 5.2 continued

Writing a short control program

Can you now write a short program to switch line 1 on for a short time and then off? The steps will be:

    switch line 1 on
    wait for some time
    switch line 1 off.

You can get a delay by using a FOR . . . NEXT loop. It is a bit like counting to 100 in a game of hide and seek before starting the search for the person hiding. (There are other ways of getting a delay, e.g. using INKEY or TIME.)

Write the following program. Press RETURN at the end of each line and do not type in the notes in brackets!

```
10 LET ?65122 = 15 (sets bits 1, 2, 4, 8 as output)
20 LET ?65120 = 1 (puts bit 1 on)
30 FOR N = 1 TO 500 (computer prints)
40 PRINT"PAUSE" the word PAUSE 500
50 NEXT N times giving delay)
60 LET ?65120 = 0 (puts bit 1 off)
70 END
```

Run your program. Does it work?

If all is well consider whether you really need the computer to print "PAUSE". Delete line 40 by typing in 40 and press RETURN. This writes a new line 40 with nothing in it.

Run your program. Note that the timing is shorter. Can you see why?

● Can you arrange a delay of about 1 sec?

Summary

You should now know that:

1 The data direction register is 65122.
2 To put a number into an address you use a ? in front of the address.
   ? means 'the contents of address . . . '
   For example
      LET ?65122 = 15 puts 15 into the data direction register and makes the first four lines outputs.
3 To control each output line, you write to a working address (65120). Each line has a particular 'bit' number such as 1, 2, 4, etc.
      ?65120 =2 would activate line 2.
   You should be able to control the switching of the first four lines. You should also be able to write a program which introduces a delay between changes.

PROBLEMS

Try writing programs to solve the following problems. Some possible solutions are given on page 91.

1 **Traffic lights**
   Use three of the output lines to stand for red, amber and green, then write a program to go through a traffic light sequence.
   (Extension:
   Write the colour on the screen as the lights change or put the colour on the screen if you have a colour monitor.)

2 **Binary counter**

Using four output bits, write a program which will go through the sequence of a binary counter, e.g.

o o o o 0
o o o • 1
o o • o 2
o o • • 3
o • 0 0 4
0 • 0 • 5, etc.

(Extension:

Write the number on the screen as the lights change.)

3 **Changing brightness**

If you switch a line on and off very quickly an indicator lamp will appear dim. You will need to do this quickly enough so as not to see the flicker.

● Can you make an indicator lamp dim?

4 **Disco lights**

Can you make a random selection of the lights using the BASIC keyword RND?

e.g. LET ?65120 = RND (15) will select at random a value between 1 and 15.

You can use a similar procedure to vary the time.

Activity 5.3

SWITCHING LAMPS AND MOTORS ON AND OFF

So far, we can do little more than control the voltage levels on the output lines. The next step is to use this **data signal** from the computer to switch lamps and motors on and off. You will have to use the theory on relays and Darlingtons which we have covered in Chapters 2 and 3.

You need:

● Marjon board (fig 5.11)
● 6 V 0.06 A lamp (with holder and connections)
● reed relay or other 5 V relays with connecting system, e.g. bread-board
● octal Darlingon chip with connecting system, e.g. breadboard
● 5 V dc supply
● (optional, 5 V motor)

1 **Lighting a lamp (direct control)**

The buffer board can be used to sink a small load current. Connect a 6 V (0.06 A) lamp as shown in fig 5.18.

You should be able to write a program to dim the lamp by switching it on and off quickly.

2 **Working a relay**

The buffer chips can sink only a small current (100 mA) so you cannot control very much directly from the buffer board. It is possible to work a reed relay (RS 349–383) in place of the lamp. This can switch the current in a separate circuit which has its own power supply. See fig 5.19. (Note the diodes to protect against induced back voltages – back emf.)

With luck, you can control other sensitive 5 V relays (RS 348–526) and RS 346–851) but these are at the limit of current which can be controlled by the buffer chips. You cannot be sure that they will work and even if they do, the buffer chips may be damaged. Being mechanical, the relays will not be too happy with very fast continuous switching.

Activity 5.3 continued

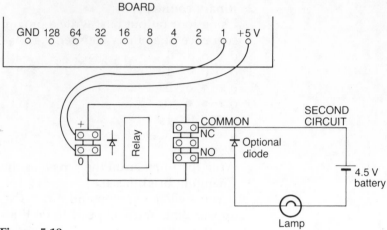

Figure 5.19

If you do not have the relays with made up connections, use a breadboard and fig 5.20 showing the internal connections. Connect the lamp so that it can be switched by the relay.

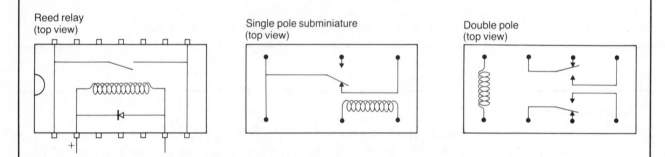

Figure 5.20

3 Using a relay, some problems

If you get a relay working, try these problems.

a Write a program to get a lamp to flash out Morse Code. 'SOS' is dot, dot, dot, dash, dash, dash, dot, dot, dot.

You can do the changes slowly.

If you listen carefully, you can hear the relay switching.

b Now write a program to see how quickly you can switch the lamp on and off. This puts some strain on the relay so do not run your program for more than a few seconds. Replacements cost about £2!

c Replace the lamp by a low voltage electric motor. You really do need a diode (IN4001) in the motor circuit to stop sparking at the relay contacts. You should be able to switch the motor on and off. Explore how quickly you can do this, but run your program for only a few seconds.

4 Passing on control through a Darlington driver

The output signal from the buffer board can be treated as data and used to control other devices through a Darlington solid state switch. The Darlington requires an insignificant current for its input control signal. This can easily be supplied from the buffer. We can use the output line to **source** this current.

Connect the circuits as shown in fig 5.21.

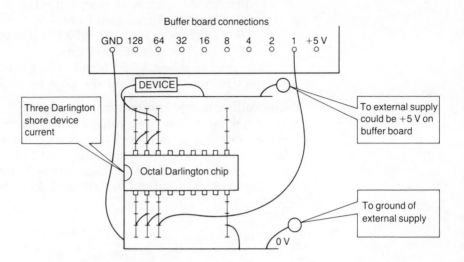

Figure 5.21

Three Darlingtons have been linked together. They share the current passing through the device. This only needs to be done for devices requiring large current.

5 **Using a Darlington, some problems**
Try the same problems given above for a relay.

6 **One final problem**
Find or build a small vehicle driven by an electric motor. Connect the motor to a control circuit.Can you write a program to move it forward 20 cm?

Solutions to these problems can be found on page 92.

Activity 5.4 (optional)

USING THE PRINTER PORT, CHELT-OUT 8-LINE OUTPUT BUFFER
This is an optional activity if you have a Chelt-out printer port buffer available. This has its own in-built Darlingtons so is ready to control a lamp or motor by simply linking them in. **The aim is to see how you can use the printer port to control 8 output lines**.
You need:
  • Chelt-out buffer board (for construction details, see page 81)
  • 6 V 0.06 A lamp
  • 5 V motor
  • 5 V dc supply
Follow through Activity 5.2 but make the following changes:
1 Connect the board to the **printer port**.
2 The leds in the array act as indicators and can be controlled from the computer.
3 The printer port has Data Direction Register at 65123 (not 65122). Begin by putting 255 into this address.

Activity 5.4 continued

4 The port working address is 65121.
5 A program to switch on lines 1 and 2 might be:
    10 ?65123 = 255 (All lines output)
    20 ?65121 = 1 (put line 1 on)
    30 FOR N = 1 TO 1000: NEXT N (Delay)
    40 ?65121 = 2 (put line 2 on)
The problems suggested for the Marjon board can be adapted for the Chelt-out board. (You should refer back to Activity 5.2.)

Controlling lamps and motors

The Chelt-out has no low voltage power supply form the printer port. So, an external dc supply 5/15 V is required to make the board work lamps and motors. Loads are connected between the +ve supply and the line output. See fig 5.22. Each line will control up to 0.5 A.

The problems you did in Activity 5.3 can be tried again here.

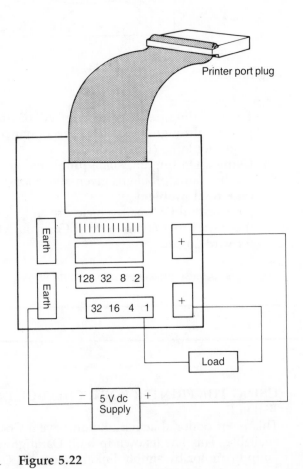

Figure 5.22

Summary

A buffer board is generally used to:
a   give some protection against misconnection
b   allow the computer data signals to control some other source of power.
Three homemade buffer boards are suggested. The Marjon is the most useful as a start.

The BBC computer has a 'Data Direction register' which determines which lines (or bits) are to be output. The address is 65122 for the user port and 65123 for the printer port.

Lines are switched on and off by writing to the working register. This address is 65120 for the user port and 65121 for the printer port.

Solutions

Problems on page 86

1 Traffic lights. Light the lamps you need by combining the control bits e.g. LET ?65120 = 3 will put on the first two lines.
One way of getting a delay is to use a FOR . . . NEXT loop.
'REM' in the program which follows stands for REMARK. The computer ignores anything following a REM statement. REMs are useful for reminding you what the program does. Do not type in my notes in brackets!

```
10 LET ?65122 = 15 (Sets data direction register)
20 LET ?65120 = 1
30 REM RED ON
40 FOR N = 1 TO 3000
50 NEXT N
60 REM DELAY
70 LET ?65120 = 2
80 REM AMBER ON
90 FOR N = 1 TO 2000
100 NEXT N
110 REM DELAY
etc.
```

2 Binary counter. You need to place a sequence of numbers in address 65120, i.e. 0, 1, 2, 3, 4, etc. You will also need some delay between the change otherwise it will happen too quickly to be seen.

```
10 LET ?65122 = 15 (Sets data direction register)
20 ?65120 = 0
30 FOR N = 1 TO 1000
40 NEXT N
50 ?65120 = 1
60 FOR N = 1 TO 1000
70 NEXT N
80 ?65120 = 2, etc.
```

If you are more experienced in programming, you might consider setting the change with a FOR . . . NEXT loop. This would give you two loops, one nested inside the other, e.g.

```
10 LET ?65122 = 15
20 FOR X = 0 TO 15
30 LET ?65120 = X
40 FOR N = 1 TO 1000
50 NEXT N
60 NEXT X
70 GOTO 20
```

3 Changing brightness. Here you simply switch a line on and off very quickly. You can vary the brightness by altering the relative time spent on and off. This is known as the 'mark-space' ratio.

```
10 LET ?65122 = 15
20 LET ?65120 = 1 (bit 1 on, mark)
30 FOR NM = 1 TO 5 (a short delay)
40 NEXT N
50 LET ?65120 = 0 (bit 1 off, space)
60 FOR N = 1 TO 2 (a shorter delay)
70 NEXT N
80 GOTO 20 (repeats the sequence)
```

4 Disco. This brief program does rather a lot!

```
10 LET ?65122 = 15
20 LET ?65120 = RND (15) (random selection of lights)
30 FOR N = 1 TO RND (300) (random time delay)
40 NEXT N
50 GOTO 20
```

Activity 5.3

1 Morse code. First, some notes on BASIC programs which solve the problems posed.

Procedures are very useful for writing structured programs. A procedure is always defined in a part of the program not directly used and called up when required.

A procedure is used in the example below to give a delay. It is defined at the end of the program in lines 220–240.

```
 10 ?65122 = 15
 20 FOR N = 1 TO 3
 30 ?65120 = 1
 40 PROCDELAY
 40 ?65120 = 0
 50 PROCDELAY
 60 NEXT N
 70 FOR N = 1 TO 3
 80 ?65120 = 1
 90 PROCDELAY
 91 PROCDELAY
 92 PROCDELAY
100 ?65120 = 0
110 PROCDELAY
120 NEXT N
130 FOR N = 1 TO 3
140 ?65120 = 1
150 PROCDELAY
160 ?65120 = 0
170 PROCDELAY
180 NEXT N
190 PROCDELAY
191 PROCDELAY
200 GOTO 20
210
220 DEF PROCDELAY
230 FOR T = 1 TO 200
240 NEXT T
250 ENDPROC
```

2 Fast switching. A suitable program is:

```
 10 ?65122 = 15
 20 ?65120 = 0
 30 PROCDELAY
 40 ?65120 = 1
 50 PROCDELAY
 60 GOTO 20
 70 DEF PROCDELAY
 80 FOR N = 1 TO * (make * a convenient number)
 90 NEXT N
100 ENDPROC
```

For fast switching a reed relay is better than the other relays. However, it is best to use a solid state switch such as a Darlington. Even so, there can be problems when you are controlling an inductive load like a motor.

The input voltage controls the current flowing into the solid state switch. If the load has a large inductance, the change in the input voltage and the linked current change may not be in phase. Inductive loads tend to slow up current changes. If the input voltage changes very quickly, you can find that the current is on when you expect it off! The system gets confused and simply does not work properly.

3 The final problem. The distance a vehicle travels can be controlled by the length of time the motor is switched on. It is a matter of trial and error to find the right time.

6 Controlling motors and running a buggy

Introduction

I well remember the first time I managed to make a computer control a motor. Somehow, it's much more satisfying than controlling lamps. We have already discussed switching a motor on and off using relays and solid state switches. In this chapter we will see now to change its direction. I will recommend two ways of doing it, one using relays and the other solid state switching.

When you have decided which system to use, I suggest building a permanent motor reverse board to control two motors. This will serve you well in many control applications. The systems cost between £8 and £16.

Full control of a motor i.e. on/off, forward/ reverse, requires two 'bits' of information. This means that you need to use two output lines from the computer.

Full control of two motors will allow you to make a buggy move forwards and backwards and turn right and left. This will require four output lines from the computer. These are readily available with the Marjon buffer board.

The chapter goes on to describe some practical ways of building and controlling a buggy.

Controlling a single motor – on/off, forward/reverse

A single motor can be controlled using relays or solid sate switches. Both were introduced in Chapter 3. Before getting down to practical details, two methods of controlling the motor need to be considered. The theory is developed in Activity 6.1.

Activity 6.1 Controlling a single motor – on/off, forward/reverse

The aim of this activity is to see how a network of switches can be arranged to control a motor.
Two methods are suggested.
This should give you an appreciation of the ways in which control is achieved in practice.
Can you sort out how each method works?
[Answers to the questions are given on page 110]

Activity 6.1 continued

Method 1 (five switch network)

You have five switches (fig 6.1).

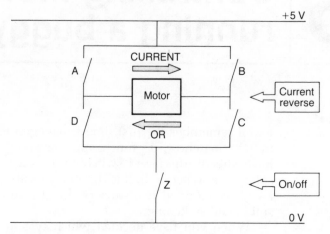

Figure 6.1

Switches A, B, C, D control the direction in which current passes through the motor.

Switch Z turns the current on and off.

    a What combination of switches should be closed for current to flow through the motor from left to right?

    b What combination would let the current flow in the reverse direction?

    c Why is it important that switches A, B, C, D and Z are not all on at the same time?

Method 2 (four switch network)

This uses four switches but only certain arrangements must be allowed. The four switches, A, B, C and D are arranged as shown in fig 6.2 (The arrangement is sometimes called a **Wheatstone** or '**H**' network. The **H** refers to the shape in which the circuit can be drawn out, fig 6.3)

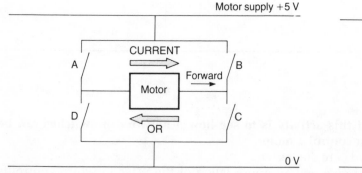

Figure 6.2

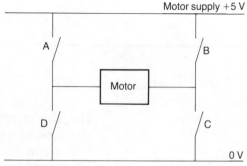

Figure 6.3

    a Can you switch the motor ON and OFF and also control the direction of current through it?

Activity 6.1 continued

b Can you complete the 'truth table' below, showing the outcome of the switch settings (0 = off and 1 = on)?
(Remember that you need a path for the current to pass through the motor and also a voltage difference (potential difference) to push it through.)

	Switch setting				Motor	
A	B	C	D	on/off	forward/reverse
0	0	0	0		
0	0	0	1		
0	0	1	0		
0	0	1	1		
0	1	0	0		
0	1	0	1		
0	1	1	0	*	*
0	1	1	1	*	*
1	0	0	1	*	*
1	0	1	0		
1	0	1	1	*	*
1	1	0	1	*	*
1	1	1	0	*	*
1	1	1	1	*	*

c The combinations are marked '*' are not allowed. Why not?
d Can you find two further combinations which have been missed out of the table?

Building working circuits

Choosing the best arrangement

If you are to control a buggy, you will want to build a permanent control board for two motors. This will link with four output data lines from a computer. Obviously, the board could be built in many ways. I will suggest two possible designs in some detail and outline a third arrangement.

In designing a board, there are a number of requirements to be met, some of which may be in competition. For the present board, it is assumed that it must:

- work reliably
- be robust
- control dc motors in a voltage range between 4 and 12 V
- be as cheap as possible
- be as easy to construct as possible

These requirements have been taken into account for the two circuits recommended. You will have to select the one which suits your needs.

Using a four switch network

At first sight, the method shown in fig 6.2 with only four switches looks the better arrangement. It can be built easily using two single pole changeover relay switches (RS 348-526). Careful organisation of the normally open and normally closed contacts will ensure that switches A and C and B and D can never be closed at the same time. See figs 6.4 and 6.5.

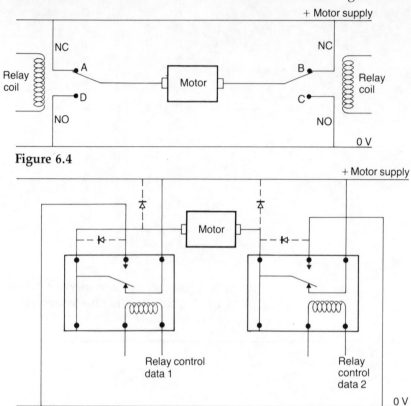

Figure 6.4

Figure 6.5

These relays may even work directly from the low power available from the Marjon board. However, the 7400 NAND output chip is not designed to sink any significant current and the few mA required to work the relay is close to or beyond the limit of the chip.

For a reliable and robust arrangement the relay coil needs a separate current supply controlled by the computer output. This is done using Darlington drivers (fig 6.6). The relays require a 5 V supply while the voltage supply for the motor will depend on the motor to be used. It could be up to 12 V.

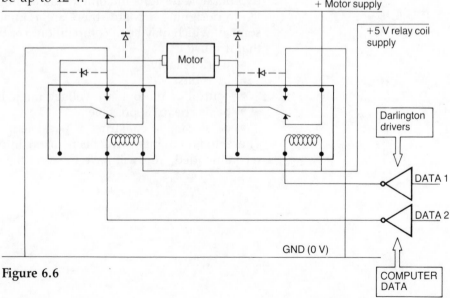

Figure 6.6

A motor control board for two motors can be built for less than £10. Details of how to do this, including making a printed circuit board are given on page 100.

However, relays have a limited life and cannot support fast continuous switching. So, a system built from solid state switches would be an improvement. One based on a four switch network which works well is described on page 96. It costs around £16 and requires soldering up a large number of components.

Using a five switch network

The method shown in fig 6.1 could offer a compromise by using a relay to change the current direction and a solid state switch for on/off.

This utilises the best attributes of each device. A double pole relay has easy connections for reversing, see fig 6.7. A Darlington gives fast on/off switching. The system costs approximately the same as the relay circuit described using a four switch network.

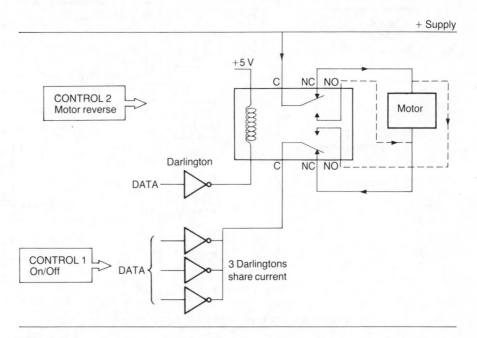

Figure 6.7

This method has a disadvantage which will not become apparent until it is used. When computers are first switched on, or the 'BREAK' key is pressed, the output control lines will be high or low voltage depending on the buffer system in use. This can result in accidently switching the motors on.

With the four switch method, the motors can only be switched on different setting between the central lines. This can only happen when a program is run. The recommended circuits are therefore, based on method two in Activity 6.1 – the four switch network.

Recommended circuits

The first circuit uses relays. It is cheaper and easier to build than the solid state system. However, the solid state system is probably more robust and preferred if you can afford it.

First recommended circuit:
Motor reverse board using
relays

Based on the method shown in fig 6.3, two motors can be controlled by four single pole changeover relays (RS348-526). The relays are switched by a Darlington driver controlled from the computer buffer board. The relay coils require 5 V which is conveniently available from the user port buffer. The motor supply voltage is separate and can be up to 12 V. (If you do not want to commit yourself to a permanent system, the circuit can be built on breadboard.)

Now perhaps is the time to consider making your own printed circuit board (pcb). If you have not made one before, it is really quite easy and satisfying. It is even more satisfying if you design your own layout. However you will find a suitable design shown in figs 6.8 and 6.9. Construction details follow. If you are building the circuit on breadboard (or stripboard), move on to page 103.

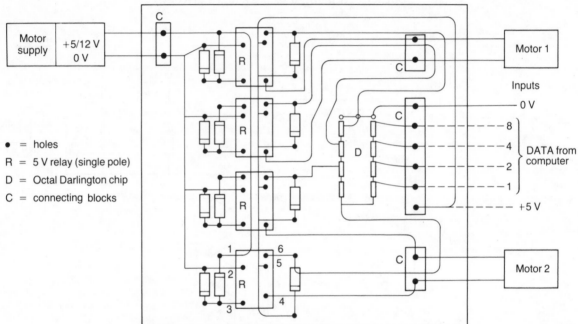

● = holes
R = 5 V relay (single pole)
D = Octal Darlington chip
C = connecting blocks

Figure 6.8   COMPONENT SIDE VIEW

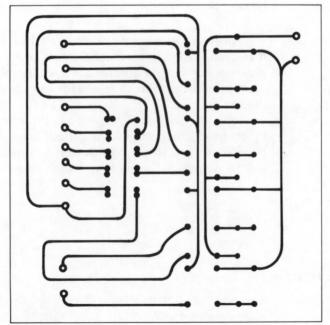

Figure 6.9   UNDERSIDE VIEW

Making a pcb by drawing and etching

Begin with a board which has a thin layer of copper on one side. This layer of copper is etched away leaving circuit connections to the components. These are soldered onto the board through appropriately drilled holes.

(1) Normally, you would plan the layout of the components and connections and draw it to scale. This has already been done in fig 6.8. (To check that you can relate this to fig 6.6 can you identify the coil connections in the bottom relay?) Most people design circuits from the top side, i.e. the component view. (By the way, the coil connections are 5 and 6.)

(2) In making a pcb you need the **underside** view of the connections. One way of getting this is to draw the top view on a transparent sheet and reverse the view. This gives rise to confusion so, take care! (I have heard that it's possible to take a photocopy of the '**top**' view and '**iron**' it onto a copper board.)

(3) For the relay motor reverse board, proceed as follows:

(a) Use a copy of the **underside** view of the circuit (fig 6.9). Place this over the copper side of the board. Mark the positions for drilling holes with a sharp instrument.

(b) Drill out the marked positions with either
    – an 0.8 mm bit for small components
    – or a 1 mm bit for larger components.
    Use a jig, e.g. a piece of stripboard, to give the positions for drilling. (Low voltage electic drills are useful here)

(c) Draw the conducting paths linking the holes on the copper side. Do this using a special felt pen or a 'permanent OHP (overhead projector) pen. Take particular care that conducting lines which are close together do not touch.

(d) Use the pen to blank out unused areas of the plate. These do not need to be etched out, saving time and chemicals.

(e) A beaker of ferric chloride solution can be heated by placing it in a bowl of hot water. Immerse the marked board in the warm ferric chloride. Agitate until only the marked areas remain. **Do not let your skin make contact with the ferric chloride and wear protective goggles.**

(f) Wash the board in warm water. Remove marker using spirit, water and abrasive pad. Inspect to ensure that no conductors are touching.

Components for relay motor reverse board

- pcb or breadboard
- 4 single pole relays 5 V   (RS348-526)
- 8 diodes IN4001   (RS261-148)
- 1 octal Darlington chip   (RS303-422)
- terminal blocks (pcb only)
- 1 6-way   (MS components 1344)
- 3 2-way   (MS components 1342)
- connecting wire (breadboard only)

You should be able to make up the circuit using fig 6.8.

The advantages of using relays are:
    relatively simple layout and cheap easy construction.
    the motor circuit voltage can be totally separated from the control circuit
The disadvantage is:
    fast continuous switching is not possible.

Second recommended circuit: Motor reverse board using solid state switching

Solid state switching uses transistors which have no moving parts. A solid state system based on the method shown in fig 6.3 is given in fig 6.10.

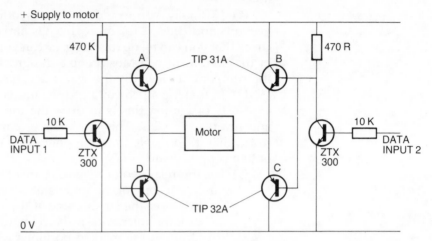

Figure 6.10

The switches are high current transistors – two types are needed npn (TIP31A) and pnp (TIP32A). The npn is switched **on** when its base is high. The pnp switches **off** when its base is high. These are worked in pairs making the switches AC and BD in fig 6.3. Low power transistors (ZTX300) control the base voltage level. In this way, transistors A and C or B and D cannot be on at the same time and cannot make a short circuit to earth. The complete circuit to control one motor is given in fig 6.11. This could be built on stripboard.

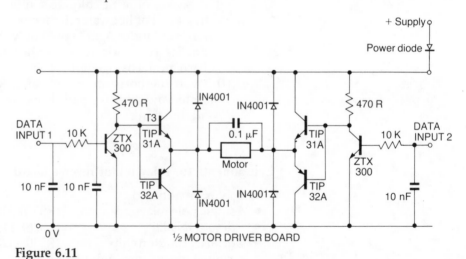

Figure 6.11

The circuit was designed at the College of St Mark and St John, and a pcb for the circuit (£3) together with constructional details can be obtained from there. Beware, I found the connections for the ZTX300 were **wrongly** shown in the details supplied and you should check the layout with fig 6.11 yourself.

To control two motors, you need:
- pcb or stripboard
- 4 TIP31As   (RS294-205)
- 4 TIP32As   (RS294-211)
- 4 ZTX300s   (RS294-457)
- 6 10 nF disc capacitors   (RS124-140)
- 2 100 nF disc capacitors   (RS124-178)
- 4 10 K resistors   (RS131-378)
- 4 470 ohm resistors   (RS131-211)
- 8 diodes IN4001   (RS261-148)
- 8 optional heatsinks   RS402-260)
- 1 power diode (optional) (Farnell BYW29-50)
- connectors e.g. barrel terminal blocks
- connecting wires
- 1 plastic box (optional)

The system will control 12 V motors by using a 15 V external supply (some voltage is 'lost' in the system). The power diode protects the system against connecting the power supply the wrong way round.

The main advantage of solid state over relays is:

can be used for fast switching – useful in speed control.

The disadvantages are:

more expensive

somewhat more complex to build.

However, I recommend the circuit to you. It works well. You ought to build the board into a plastic box for protection (see figs 6.12 and 6.13).

Figure 6.12

Figure 6.13

Controlling a buggy

Now that you have reversing system for two motors, you can control a buggy. It is a good example of a genuine control system and can give a great deal of satisfaction.

Making the buggy

There are two principal ways of building a buggy which can move forwards and backwards and turn left and right. The most common is to have two independent traction wheels driven by two geared down electric motor (fig 6.14). The same principle is used in a hand cranked paddle boat. An alternative is to have one motor controlling traction and another controlling steering (fig 6.15) – like a road roller.

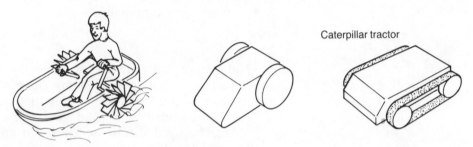

Caterpillar tractor

Figure 6.14

There are many ways of building buggies. The materials can be specially purchased items, junk or construction kits. If you decide to build your own from simple materials, take care to organise a considerable gearing down of the electric motor. See fig 6.16. This is needed so that your vehicle is strong enough to carry extra components and sensors later.

The easiest and quickest way is to use a '**Big Track**' motor system. It needs two wheels connected to the drives, large coffee jar lids suit the purpose well. Make holes in the middle with a soldering iron. Take care not to breathe in the fumes. Fix the wheels in place with a glue gun.

Traction can be improved by adding rubber bands to the outside of the wheels and increasing their weight by adding plasticine to the inside. The third wheel can simply be a 'skid' e.g. a drawing pin glue-gunned into place, but you may wish to devise a better solution.

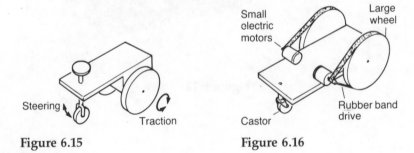

Figure 6.15

Figure 6.16

The 'Big Track' motor system includes gears and a cleaver magnetic 'clutch'. The clutch locks the two wheels together so that the buggy will move in a straight line. The lock is broken when the motors drive in opposite directions for turning a corner. It needs a supply of about 6 V dc.

A cheap buggy construction kit can also be bought from NESTEC (fig 6.17) at around £5. It is, however, quite small and is not so easily adapted for further applications. Another realistic possibility is to use Lego or Fischer-Technik e.g. two Lego motors running caterpillar tracks make a simple buggy. These kits are, however, quite expensive (figs 6.18, 6.19). Of these, I recommend the 'Big Track' motor in spite of its recent price increase.

Assuming that you have a buggy, the next activity discusses how it can be controlled from the computer.

Figure 6.17

Figure 6.18

Figure 6.19

Activity 6.2

Controlling a buggy from the computer

This activity assumes that you have a buggy available together with a motor reverse board. **The aim is to see how the computer can control movement of the buggy and write some programs to do this.**
You need:

- buggy with two independent motors which can control forward, reverse, right and left hand turns.
- dc power supply for motors e.g. 6 V for 'Big Track'
- motor reverse box for controlling two motors (solid state or relay)
- long length (at least 2 m) of cable with 8 or more lines (for later developments)
- Computer user port control board (e.g. Marjon system)
- connecting system e.g. barrel terminal blocks.

1 Start building up your connections from the buggy motors. Spend time making your connections robust and reliable. Make sure they cannot touch other connections. This will save much frustration later. I strongly recommend glue-gunning barrel terminal blocks to any home made buggy.
2 Check that the motors work by direct connection to the supply.
3 It pays to make the connections in a systematic way. As you add additional parts, check that everything works.

Activity 6.2 continued

4 Continue by connecting the motor reverse system to your buggy. For the relay system, see fig 6.20. For the solid state system, see fig 6.21. Add the supply voltage making sure the polarity is correct. Before you connect anything else, check that the controls work by taking each data input line to high and low voltage. (If your motor reverse box contains relays, these run on 5 V)

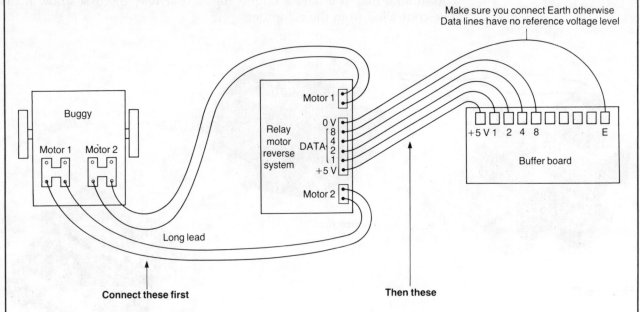

Figure 6.20

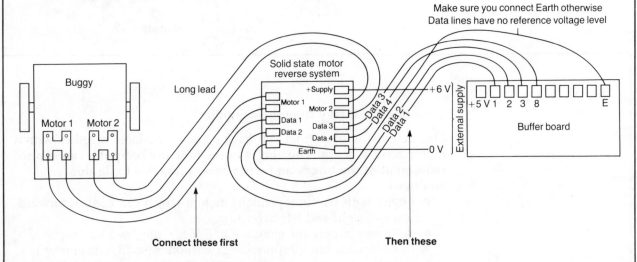

Figure 6.21

5 Now, connect the data inputs to the computer buffer board.
6 Sort out the computer output values which make the buggy move forwards, backwards, turn right and left. This will depend on how you have connected the motors and is best discovered by trying all possible output combinations.

Activity 6.2 continued

7 A program like this could help:

```
10   ?65122=15
20   INPUT X
30   ?65120=X
40   GOTO 20
```

X takes values 0 to 15

8 Keep a note of the important values.

9 There is quite a lot you can do with the buggy so keep the buggy, motor reverse and output buffer connected up for as long as possible.

Making the buggy do something

Can you make the buggy do some of these?

a Move forward 50 cm

b Turn through 90°

c Move around a square, coming back to the starting place

d Move around a path drawn on the floor

e Go into its 'home' – a cardboard box

f Do a three-point turn

The way to do all this is to write a program which makes the buggy do something for a set length of time. In other words, **a delay** is built into your program, before it moves onto a new instruction.

Time delays can be made using FOR . . . NEXT loops (but you can also do it using TIME or INKEY)

You will need to experiment to find the appropriate delay times.

If you need further help the following program should be useful.

Moving round a square.

```
10   ?65122=15 : REM data direction register
20   PRINT "PRESS 'RETURN' TO START"
30   INPUT X: REM wait for key to be pressed
40   ?65120=5: REM FORWARD
50   FOR N=1 TO 1000: NEXT N: REM delay
60   ?65120=6: REM TURN LEFT
70   FOR N=1 TO 1500: NEXT N: REM delay to turn 90
90   ?65120=5: REM FORWARD
              , etc.
```

Notes on the program:

1 You will have to decide on the delay times and output lines which suit you.
2 The symbol: separates instructions in the same line
3 REM means that what follows is a remark and is not acted on by the computer. It's good working practice to use REM statements to remind you what a line does.
4 Since 'forward, turn left' is repeated four times, you could simply repeat this set of instructions four times using a FOR . . . NEXT loop e.g.

```
35  FOR X=1 TO 4

80  NEXT X
```

Use X rather than N in this four times loop.
What would happen if you used N?
You could also use a REPEAT . . . UNTIL loop.

The need for feedback

You will probably have noticed that the buggy is not very reliable in moving precisely as required. For example, in going round a square, it doesn't end back at the starting place. You really need to pass some information about position back to the computer so that correcting action can be taken. This is called 'feedback'.

One way of doing this is to make yourself part of the feedback loop; i.e. keep watch on the buggy and give instructions to make it move to the required place. This is quite useful for developing your programming skills. Later on, this will be done automatically using electrical sensors.

Can you make the buggy move under instructions from the keyboard?

Moving under keyboard control

The GET$ statement is useful here 'G$=GET$' gives a delay. The computer waits until a key is pressed. When this happens, G$ equals the character pressed. To see how it works, try this program:

```
10  G$=GET$

20  PRINT G$

30  GOTO 10
```

Run the program.
● What happens as you press the keys?
Notice that you don't have to press 'RETURN' as you would if using INPUT X.
● What happens when you press 'SPACE BAR'?
The $ means that you are working with characters rather than numbers.

(There is also a GET statement which works in numbers.)
Now make the computer do something depending on the character in G$.

Add 25 IF G$="2" THEN PRINT "TWO"

Note the speech marks around 2 – these indicate you are using the character 2 and not the number 2.
● Does the program work?
What happens if you press 'SPACE BAR'?

Add 26 IF G$=" " THEN PRINT"SPACE BAR PRESSED"

● What happens?
I hope that's enough to get you started using your buggy.

You could use the following keys to control the buggy:

F – forward
B – backwards
R – turn right
L – turn left
S – stop

but they are difficult to find quickly.

So, I suggest using:

B – forward
SPACE BAR – backwards
V – turn right
N – turn left
S – stop

as these keys are close together and easier to find.

Your program should:

- continue with the previous instruction until a key is pressed
- note the key pressed
- change the output instruction in response
- wait for another key to be pressed

Try it yourself. My suggestion for a program is as follows.

```
10   ?65122=15

20   G$=GET$

30   IF G$="B" THEN ?65120=5      :REM forward

40   IF G$=" " THEN ?65120=10     :REM backwards

50   IF G$="V" THEN ?65120=9      :REM turn left

60   IF G$="N" THEN ?65120=6      :REM turn right

70   IF G$="S" THEN ?65120=0      :REM stop

80   GOTO 20
```

You will need to choose the right numbers in address 65120 for your system. You can test it first by looking at the indicator lamps on the output lines.

Can you print the current instruction on the screen?

(Experienced programmers may like to make the grey arrow keys control the buggy – but this is not for beginners.)

You should now be able to connect a buggy to a motor reverse system and buffer board so that the computer can control the movement of the buggy. The next step is to use automatic feedback control using electronic sensors.

Summary

A **motor reverse board** – made up of relays or solid state switches – is needed for full control of current flow through a motor.

Switching a motor on/off and making it go forwards/ reverse requires two '**bits**' of data and two computer output lines.

It's very useful to have a permanent motor reverse board for control of two motors. (Two methods are recommended, one using relays and the other solid state switching.)

The movement of a buggy (on/off, forward/reverse) can be completely controlled using two motors. This needs four output lines from the computer.

A computer program can give a sequence of movement instructions.

In practice, a buggy will not behave precisely as instructed. Correcting action can only be taken if there is some kind of 'feedback' of information.

A person can provide feedback information by controlling the movements of a buggy through the computer keyboard.

In BASIC, the G$=GET$ instruction will wait until a key is pressed. The key pressed becomes G$.

Solutions

Activity 6.1

In both methods you have to avoid a short circuit to earth. In **method 1**, if Z is closed then A and D or B and C must not be on at the same time.

It is similar for method 2. These combinations have been marked '*' in the table.

The missing combinations are 1 0 0 0 and 1 1 0 0.

In method 1, current flows from left to right through the motor if A, D and Z are switched on.

It flows in the reverse direction if B, C and Z are used.

In **method 2**, it turns out that there are only two combinations which switch the motor on. Switches A and D 'on' give forward motion and B and C 'on' give reverse.

The other combinations do not complete a circuit through the motor to earth.

7 Linking with a BBC computer – inputs to the user port

Introduction

Up to now we have been using the computer to control events. This is only part of the story. When we can feed electronic data back into the computer we will have complete control. This chapter explores how to input data to the computer through the user port. We will use the Marjon buffer board built previously. If you want to refresh your memory see Chapter 5 for details of how this was done.

In addition, construction details for an 8-line input board will be given. After sorting out how to operate the inputs a microswitch and light sensor will be used to gain full control of a buggy.

Constructing buffer boards

If you have followed through Chapter 5, then the construction of the buffer board has mostly been done. Both the demonstration board and the Marjon board can be used for inputs. Their construction has already been described in Chapter 5, see page 76.

If at a later stage, you need more than four input lines, all 8 user port lines can be operated as inputs with the Chelt-in board.

A Chelt-in board could be used alongside the Chelt-out board which links to the printer port. These give you eight outputs and eight inputs. Instructions for how to construct a Chelt-out 8 line output were also given in Chapter 5, page 81.

Building the Chelt-in board (8-line User port input)

You need:
- stripboard 2.5 mm pitch, 9 cm × 9 cm (RS433–826)
- 1 20-way IDC ribbon cable plug (RS467–289)
- 0.5 m 20-way ribbon cable (RS360–122) (Farnell and Maplin supply cable in short lengths)
- 1 24 pin DIL stripboard connector (RS468–276)
- 1 74LS245 buffer chip (RS308–348)
- 1 20-way chip socket (for buffer chip) (RS402–210)
- 4 4-way DIL terminal blocks (Farnell 146–258) (or terminal block connections)
- single-strand insulated connecting wire

The Chelt-in board is built on stripboard as shown in fig 7.1. To do this make 21 breaks in the copper strips, at the points marked **X** in the figure. The layout is designed for minimum soldering. Complete the soldering to the stripboard then connect the ribbon cable to the board. After this, connect the plug, taking special care to connect it the right way round.

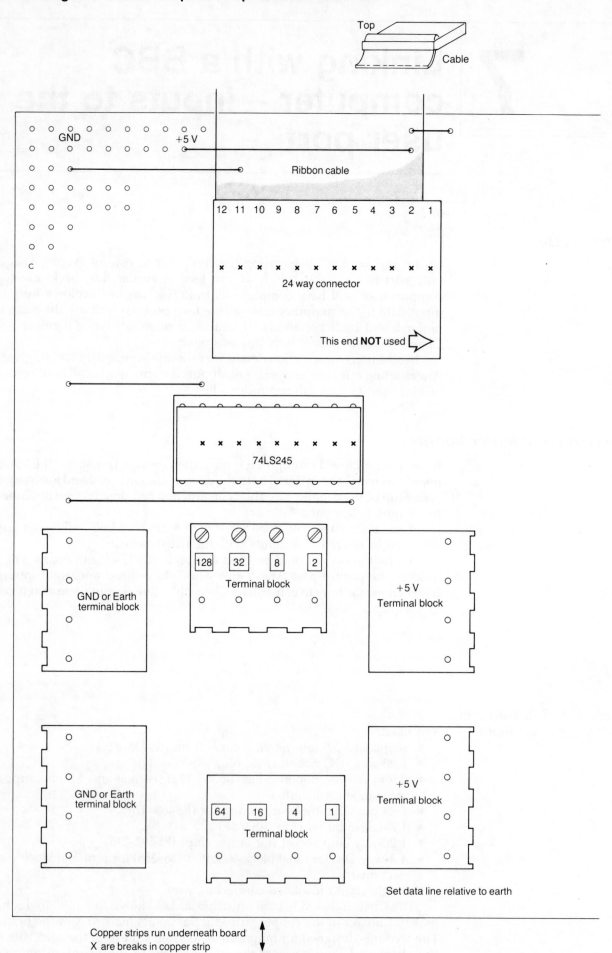

Figure 7.1

The 74LS245 buffer chip is an octal transceiver. See fig 7.2. (Octal means eight lines. Trans means across, so a **transceiver** carries information across the chip.) A **'transceiver'** carries information across. Data can travel in either direction. Pin 1 is kept at +5 V. This sets the direction for data flow, in this case, into the computer. Pin 20 is the chip supply voltage and also needs to be at +5 V. Pin 10 is earth/ground for this chip. Pin 19 is the chip enable and is active for logic 0.

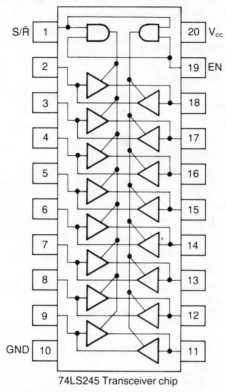

74LS245 Transceiver chip

Figure 7.2

Putting data into the user port

The first activity depends on whether you have built a demonstration board. (Construction details were given in Chapter 5.) If you haven't built a demonstration board then start at Activity 7.2. This shows how to input data and can be completed quite quickly. The activities which follow introduce you to using a microswitch and light sensor to input information.

Activity 7.1

PRACTICAL INTRODUCTION TO INPUTS – using the demonstration board
This activity explores how voltage levels on the User port lines can pass information into the computer.
You need:
- demonstration board
- connecting wires
- optional 10 K potentiometer (variable resistor)
- optional 0–5 V dc voltmeter

Remember that the demonstration board makes a direct connection to the user port of the computer – so take care. The input signals **MUST NOT EXCEED** 5 V. Since there is no buffer protection in this board do not use any voltage other than the 0 V and +5 V provided by the user port. Plug in your board.

Activity 7.1 continued

1 Begin by making all lines input.

Do this by making the contents of the data direction register equal zero. For the BBC computer the data direction register has an address number of 651220. Type:

    LET ?65122=0 then press RETURN

In practice, you probably wouldn't need to do this. The **default** setting of the Data Direction Register (65122) is zero. The 'default' setting means that this is the natural setting, when no other instructions have been given.

Your instruction makes non of the lines output, – in other words, they are all inputs!

The input data appears in address 65120 – the same one that we used for outputs.

2 To find out what number is in address 65120 type:

    PRINT ?65120 then press RETURN

You can repeat this with the program below.

        10 LET ?65122=0
        20 PRINT ?65120
        30 GOTO 20

Run this program and the contents of 65120 should be continuously printed down the screen.

> *Transistor logic is often said to 'float high'. This means that if no particular signal is presented to an input, it behaves as if it were high.*

Does the number you have in 65120 tell you that all inputs (1, 2, 4, 8, 16, 32, 64, 128) are high?

What happens when you connect line 1 to +5 V (fig 7.3)? Does the number change?

Now connect line 1 to 0 V.

• Do you get 254?

Connect other port bits to earth. Can you see a pattern in the number you get?

Is the bit value subtracted from 255?

If you want a number showing the value of the bit which is earthed, change line 20 to:

    20 PRINT (255–?65120)

Does it work?

Optional extension

Connect the potentiometer to make a voltage divider. Find out the critical voltage which switches the input.

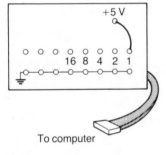

Figure 7.3

Some Revision

a Each input line carries one '**bit**' of information and has its own bit '**value**', e.g. 16, 32, 64, 128.

b The information is held in address 65120 (the user port working register).

c For the Marjon buffer board, computer inputs are activated by pulling the input line down to zero voltage. When this happens, the bit value is added to the contents of memory location 65120.

d The data direction register sets which lines are inputs. The data on the input lines cannot be changed from the keyboard.

An aside on the way the buffer board works

You may find it strange that you need to earth the input to activate a line. The reason is that the buffer acts as an inverter

   When the input is low, the computer receives a high voltage.

   When the input is high, the computer receives a zero.

The buffer is built with a transistor–transistor logic (TTL) chip containing NAND gates. These act as inverters. In TTL logic, unconnected lines float high. So, if you do nothing to alter any of the inputs, all inputs to the buffer are high. These are inverted by the NAND gates in the buffer board and the computer receives a low voltage on all lines. Hence, a reading of zero. However, if you earth one of the buffer input lines the voltage the computer receives is inverted and reported in address 65120. A fuller explanation of the Marjon buffer board design is given in Chapter 9.

Activity 7.2

INPUTS THROUGH THE USER PORT – using the Marjon buffer board

You know how to control output lines. **In this activity you will see how to work the user port input lines.**

You need:

- Marjon buffer board
- connecting wires

Carefully plug your buffer board into the user port. We are going to see how you can change the number in address 65120 by changing the voltage level on an input line. Address 65120 is the same memory location that you used for outputs.

You must do two things first:

1 Use the data direction register (65122) to set the first four lines or 'bits' as output and the remaining four as inputs.

2 Start with zero in register 65120 so that you do not confuse input data with any numbers already there.

It is best to write a short program to save having to keep typing in instructions. Type:

10 LET ?65122=15	(15 sets lines 1, 2, 4, 8 as outputs and the remaining 4 lines – 16, 32, 64, 128 – as inputs. If you have another buffer box, use a number to suit it.)
20 LET ?65120=0	(Empties any previous numbers from memory location 65120.)
30 PRINT ?65120	(Prints the contents of register 65120.)
40 GOTO 30	(This is a loop which keeps printing the contents of 65120.)

Now run the program. You should see a number repeated down the screen.

Can you change this number by connecting data bit 16 to high (5 V) and then low voltage (0 V)? – see fig 7.4. Note how you get the numbers in the address.

4 Try the other input lines.

- What numbers appear in address 65120?
- How can you get 48, 128, 144, 112 into 65120? (You will need more than one connecting wire to do it.)

5 Complete these sentences:

When bit value 16 is connected to *high* voltage (5 V) the number in address 65120 is . . .

When bit value 16 is connected to *low* voltage (0 V) the number in address 65120 is . . .

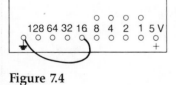

Figure 7.4

Activity 7.2 continued

Separating input and output data

6 What happens when you write numbers into address 65120 from the keyboard?

For example, the first four bit values (1, 2, 4, 8) are outputs and you have already used them.

Begin by writing 1 into address 65120, so change line 20 in the previous program to:

   20 LET ?65120=1

Run the program.

- What happens as you make the connection to port bit 16 high and low?

Try using port bit 32.

Write other numbers (up to 15) at program line 20.

- Can you see a pattern?

7 Is it true that the number in 65120 is made up by adding the input to any number already there?

8 What happens if you try and write 16 into address 65120?

Activity 7.3

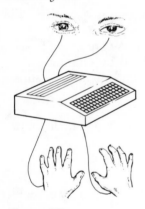

Figure 7.5

USING SWITCHES FOR INPUT

You can easily use sensors to make your computer 'feel' and 'see' (fig 7.5). **The aim here is to link switches to the computer through the user port**. We will then try some practical problems to give you practice in writing programs.

You can buy lever operated microswitches (fig 7.6). A long lever makes the switch sensitive. They usually have three connections – common (C) normally open (NO) and normally closed (NC). You need the common and NO connections for present use. You can easily make microswitches from simple materials such as paper clips, drawing pins or aluminium kitchen foil mounted on to a piece of folded stiff card (fig 7.7).

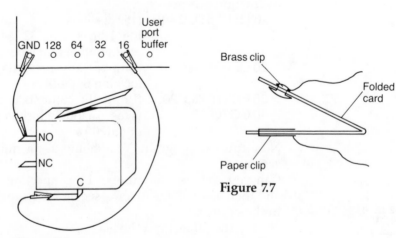

Figure 7.6

Figure 7.7

For some practical problems using switches
You need:

- user port buffer board (e.g. Marjon)
- 2 microswitches (RS337–863) or homemade switches)
- connecting wires
- 1 1 uF capacitor

Activity 7.3 continued

1 Using a switch

Use a microswitch, or more simply a wire, to make contact between one input line and earth on the user port buffer (fig 7.6)

- Can you write a program which indicates whether your switch is open or closed?

Hint: Assume that the address 65120 will contain one number (say A) when the switch is open and another (say B) when it's closed. (A) will normally be zero and (B) will depend on which port bit you have chosen.

I suggest that you print **'open'** on the screen when ?65120=A and **'closed'** when ?65120=B. (Remember that in BBC basic ? means 'the contents of address . . . '.)

If you want further help, see page 124.

2 Can you cope with two switches?

Add a second microswitch or wire to control a second input line. There are now four possible values for ?65120. These correspond to:

switch 1	switch 2	
off	off	both off
off	on	switch 2 on
on	off	switch 1 on
on	on	both on

Find the contents of 65120 by exploring the switch settings.

Write a program to report the situation on the screen.

Hint: This is an extension of the first program with four rather than two possible readings for ?65120.

A solution is given on page 124.

3 Counting the number of times a switch is closed

Use a single mechanical switch connected as before.

Can you write a program to count how many times it is switched on?

Hint: The logic could be as follows:

Assume that you have two possible readings – (A) switch open and (B) switch closed.

Count the number of times A changes to B.

Let this number be 'N'. It must start at 0.

Look at ?65120

If ?65120=A then do nothing and look again at ?65120

If ?65120=B then increase N by 1

but, take care! You must not count again until the switch has returned to its first setting. In other words ?65120 must first return to A. When it changes to B another count is made. Try your own solution first. If you get stuck have a look at the one given on page 124.

Switch bounce

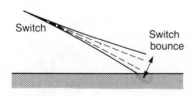

Figure 7.8

In activity 7.3 in spite of making sure that you did not continue to count when the switch was closed you may have found that your counting seemed to 'run on' and was unreliable. This is a common effect with mechanical switches. The switch does not switch on and off cleanly. It **'bounces'** rapidly on and off for a short time (fig 7.8). As the computer program works very quickly you can easily get extra counts. Switch bounce can be overcome in two ways:

a adapt the program (software)

b alter the electronics (hardware)

Software

Try adapting your program by introducing a short delay before returning to testing for a closed switch, e.g. use a FOR . . NEXT loop. By doing this you effectively switch the system off for a short time and hope that any 'bouncing' finishes in the time the system is switched off.

Hardware

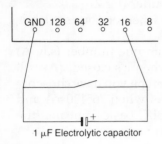

1 μF Electrolytic capacitor

Figure 7.9

Try a hardware solution by introducing a 1 uF capacitor across the switch contacts (fig 7.9). Take care to connect it the right way round. A capacitor should smooth out changes in voltage.

Other hardware methods of overcoming switch bounce are:

a) using a Schmitt trigger

The Schmitt trigger is a collection of components which have some in-built feedback of voltage from the output to the input. The important point is that there are two reference levels on the input side. If the input voltage is rising, the system does not switch until the upper level has been exceeded (fig 7.10). It will not switch back until the voltage falls below the lower level. So, if the voltage has some limited fluctuation the system will only switch once.

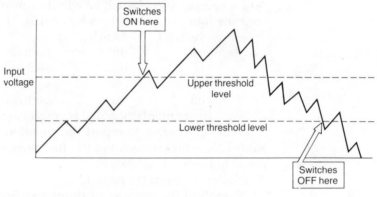

Figure 7.10

A Schmitt trigger can be obtained in chip form as a 2 input NAND gate, e.g. 74LS132 (TTL +5 V supply) or 4093B (CMOS +3 to +15 V supply (fig 7.11). Join the two inputs to make an inverter. (For more about TTL and CMOS see Chapter 9, page 152.)

The circuits shown in fig 7.12 use a capacitor to smooth out rapid voltage changes. Switch bounce should be overcome when this is combined with a Schmitt trigger.

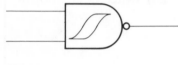

Figure 7.11

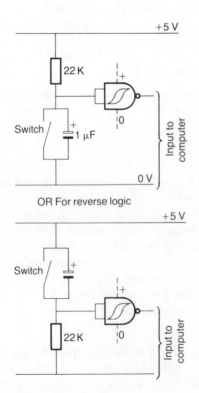

Figure 7.12

b   using two NAND gates
Another way of dealing with bounce in a microswitch uses two NAND gates in a 7400 chip. It involves feedback. Both the NO and NC terminals on the switch are connected. The circuit is shown in fig 7.13. You will find that explaining how it works is quite a challenge.

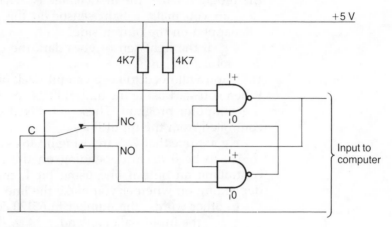

Figure 7.13

Activity 7.4

USING LIGHT SENSORS FOR INPUT
The aim here is to connect a light sensor and use it to control the output lines.
You need:
- A sensor such as a ldr (ORP12) or a phototransistor
- user port buffer which receives inputs (Marjon or Chelt-in)
- 6 V 0.06 A lamp in holder
- (optional 4.5 V motor, controlling relay and supply voltage)
- connecting wires

Connect the sensor (ldr or phototransistor) between bit 16 and earth (fig 7.14). Then you should be able to change the number in address 65120 by changing the light level. When the light level is high you are effectively taking the input voltage to earth level. (A phototransistor responds to light changes much more quickly than a ldr. It only works one way round, so if your circuit does not work, reverse the connections. You may need a reasonably bright light. A 6 V 0.06 A lamp connected between earth and the 5 V supply on the buffer board may be sufficient.)

We will see later how you can make the response sensitive to different light levels.

Some practical problems with a light sensor
1 Write a program which will report on the screen whether a sensor is in light or darkness.
Hint: Connect the sensor between input line 16 and earth.
Brightness should give 16 in address 65120 and darkness 0. Use an IF . . . THEN statement to print the condition on the screen.
For an example solution see page 119.

2 **Use a light sensor to count how many times your hand passes across the sensor.**
Hint: The program will be similar to the counting problem in Activity 7.3.

Although there is no mechanical switch, you may find behaviour similar to **'switch bounce'**, i.e. more changes are counted than you expect.

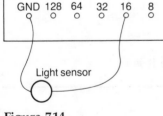

GND 128 64 32 16   8

Light sensor

Figure 7.14

Activity 7.4 continued

It depends on how the light cuts in and out across the sensor and also on how the electric circuit responds to this change. (An edge which cuts off light has associated diffraction fringes. Fast acting components like phototransistors can respond to them. You can solve this difficulty by making the circuit 'blind' for a short time, i.e. introduce a delay into the program when the first change is detected.)

3 Can you make a light sensor on the input side make something happen on the output side?

e.g. if the light sensor goes dark the computer switches a light or motor on.

Hint: You will need to keep careful track of the numbers in 65120.

When you start using the output lines you put numbers into 65120 from the computer program. These get mixed up with numbers which are controlled from the input lines.

e.g assume that you are using bit 16 as an input line. You can expect ?65120 to be 0 or 16 depending on the input logic state. If you are controlling an output line using bit 1, then ?65120 would be 0 or 1, depending on whether you make the line off or on.

In other words, the number in 65120 comes from two sources:

the input data (16) and
the output data (1)

The two bits add together in address 65120. Depending on the settings, you could have 0, 1, 16, 17.

Using two bits, the number of possible combinations is small. When more bits are involved it can get quite complicated.

You can separate out bits using the 'logical AND'. This acts like a kind of mask which screens out all bits except those wanted (fig 7.15). To look at bit 16 in address 65120 write:

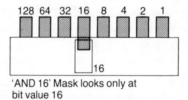

'AND 16' Mask looks only at
bit value 16

Figure 7.15

PRINT (?65120 AND 16)

If bit 16 is high your answer is 16. Otherwise it is 0.

You don't *have* to use the 'logical AND', there are other ways. However, it does make life easier when you have more than two inputs. For an explanation of how it works see Chapter 9, page 150.

For a possible program solution see page 125.

Flowcharts

Perhaps it is appropriate to mention flowcharts here. A typical flowchart is shown in fig 7.16. The shapes of the symbols used are always the same for the same type of function indicated in the flowchart. Flowcharts have many uses, not only in the writing of computer programs. They are useful in sorting out any set of complex instructions. In a computer program a flowchart is useful in determining the structure of a program. The flowchart on the left-hand side of fig 7.16 gives the logic sequence to be used in Activity 7.5.

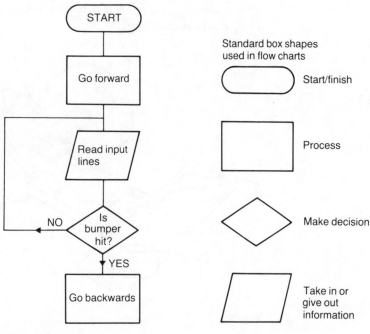

Figure 7.16

Buggy with a control system

You can make a buggy move forwards and back and turn left and right by controlling two motors.

You need to link the buggy to a motor reverse board which is controlled by the computer buffer board.

In practice, movement isn't precisely controlled. There are slight variations each time. There is no reporting back of position to the computer. (This is called 'open loop' control.)

You really need to pass some information about position back to the computer so that corrective action can be taken. When this happens, you have 'feedback' and 'closed loop' control. You can do this by attaching sensors to the buggy. These can be switches or light sensors which are then connected to the user port.

Buggy with feedback

You are now in a position to build a complete buggy control system. In Chapter 6 we developed a motor reverse board. You now know how to link a switch and light sensor to the user port. If you attach sensors to the buggy you can use the computer as a flexible controller acting on feedback from the sensors.

The next two activities give advice about some of the things you can do.

Activity 7.5

A BUGGY WITH FEEDBACK
The aim of this activity is to give you experience of using switches for control. You will then be ready to develop some more sophisticated control systems.

Reporting back on buggy position using switches
The easiest way is to fix one or two microswitches on the front of your buggy. Use ones which have long levers to act as **'feelers'**, see fig 7.17. When these are connected to the input lines you can tell when the buggy hits something.

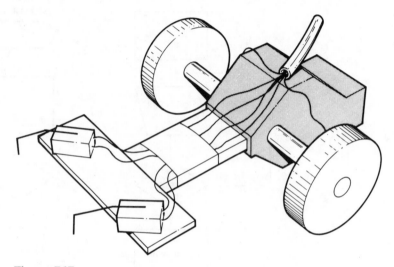

Figure 7.17

You need:
- user port buffer board (Marjon)
- motor reverse system
- buggy with at least 2 m of 9-way cable
- supply for buggy motors (batteries will do, e.g. 4.5 V, but a low-voltage power pack is more reliable)
- 2 microswitches or homemade switches
- connecting wires

Can you make your buggy go forward and then reverse when it hits a barrier?
The logic sequence would be:

go forward
read input lines
if switches are activated then reverse,
otherwise continue forward.

It's easiest to have only one sensor on the front of your buggy and this, perhaps, is the best way to start. However, I will assume that yours has two 'feelers'.

If only one of the feelers touches the barrier, the program will not work.
Can you find a way to overcome this?
See page 125 for solutions to these problems.

Activity 7.6

Some suggestions for practical projects
You should now be able to develop a number of control projects. Some suggestions follow. You may have different ideas.
You need:
- user port buffer board (Marjon)
- motor reverse system
- buggy with at least 2 m of 9-way cable
- supply for buggy motors (batteries will do, e.g. 4.5 V, but a low-voltage power pack is more reliable)
- 2 microswitches or homemade switches
- connecting wires
- ligh sensor (ldr– ORP12)
- 10 K variable resistor ('pot')

1 **Can you make the buggy steer round a brick?**
   On touching, it needs to back off, move sideways and have another go.

2 **Keeping a buggy on a table top.**
   Microswitches can also be used to tell when the buggy has reached the edge of a table (fig 7.17). If you have two switches, you can tell which side of the buggy is nearest the edge. You can then back off and turn away from the edge. If you want help a sample program to do this in BBC basic is given on page 125.

3 **Finding its way home.**
   Set up a fence and a cardboard box as 'home' (fig 7.18). Make the buggy feel its way around the fence until it finds home. Can you add a light sensor to report when it has got there and make it stop?

Figure 7.18

4 **Finding a white sheet of paper on the floor then stopping.**
   Use a light sensor to detect light reflected from the floor. You will need to be able to adjust the sensitivity of the sensor, possibly by using a potential divider system (fig 7.19). Variation in the ambient light level may be a problem.
   Should the buggy carry its own lamp?
   Make the buggy move forward and then get it to stop at the white paper.
   You can extend this to devise a program to make the buggy scan the floor area looking for the white paper.
   It sounds easy, but making it work reliably is quite a challenge.

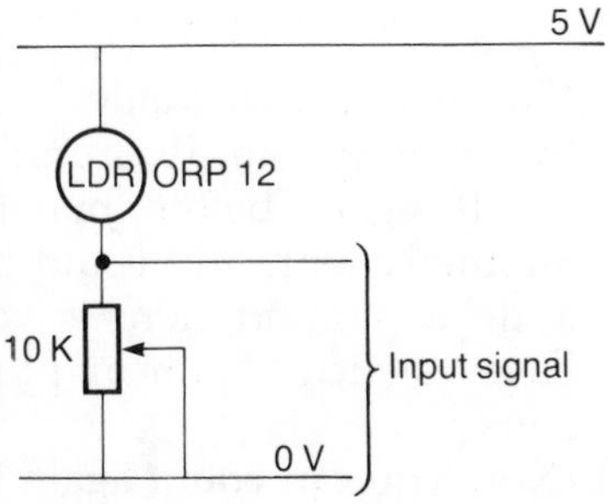

5 V

LDR ORP 12

10 K   Input signal

0 V

Figure 7.19

Summary

Data into the BBC user port uses address 65120.

The Data Direction Register (65122) sets which lines are outputs. A zero bit value makes a line input. (If no setting is made ?65122=0. This is the default value and all lines are input.)

Input data is held in the user port working address (65120) The Marjon buffer board works by earthing input lines.

Switches and light sensors can be used to detect 'touch' and light levels.

Switch bounce sometimes occurs. It can be taken into account in the software or cured with additional electronics.

A particular bit value in address 65120 can be selected using the logical AND. This acts as a mask.

Solutions

Activity 7.3

1 using one switch

```
10 LET ?65122=15
20 LET ?65120=0        (Sets zero in 65120 – just in case there is a number
                        remaining from a previous program.)
30 LET X=?65120        (X is the number found in address 65120)
35 PRINT X             (shows value of X)
40 IF X=A THEN PRINT"OPEN"  (put in your own value for A)
50 IF X=B THEN PRINT"CLOSED" (put in your own value for B)
60 GOTO 30
```

2 using two switches

A = value when both switches off (normally = 0)
B = value of first line number (e.g. 16)
C = value of second line number (e.g. 32)

Change the previous program as follows putting in your own numbers for A, B and C:

```
40 IF X=A THEN PRINT"NO SWITCHES ON"
50 IF X=B THEN PRINT"SWITCH 1 ON"
55 IF X=C THEN PRINT"SWITCH 2 ON"
57 IF X=B + C THEN PRINT "BOTH SWITCHES ON"
```

A = contents of 65120 when switch is open (off)
B = contents of 65120 when switch is closed (on)

```
10 LET ?65122=15
20 LET ?65120=0
30 LET N=0: REM N = COUNT NUMBER
40 LET X=?65120        (X becomes number found in
                        address (65120)
50 IF X=A THEN GOTO 40 (Return to 40 if switch is off –
                        put in your own value for A.)
60 N=N + 1             (Increase count by 1)
70 PRINT N
80 LET X=?65120
90 IF X=B THEN GOTO 80 (Put in your own value for B.
                        Switch is still on. Wait until it
                        is off again before making
                        another count. You could try
                        a delay around here if you
                        have switch bounce prob-
                        lems.)
100 IF X=A THEN GOTO 40 (Now you can count again.)
```

Activity 7.4

example solution:
```
10 LET ?65122=15
20 LET ?65120=0                    (Sets zero in 65120)
30 LET X=?65120
40 IF X=16 THEN PRINT"BRIGHT"
50 IF X=0 THEN PRINT"DARK"
60 GOTO 30
```

Possible program solution
```
10 ?65122=15
20 ?65120=0
30 IF (?65120 AND 16)=16 THEN LET ?65120=1 (logical AND selects
    bit 16 only bit 1 is switched on when sensor dark)
40 IF (?65120 AND 16)=0 THEN ?65120=0 (bit 1 switched off when
    sensor bright)
50 GOTO 30
```

Activity 7.5

A program for reversing on hitting a barrier
Assume that switches are connected to input lines 16 and 32. If both are pressed the number 48 is returned.
For output control, assume that 5 is forward and 10 reverse.
Your system may use different lines and you will have to make appropriate changes.
```
10 ?65122=15
20 ?65120=5:REM forward
30 IF ?65120=53 THEN ?65120=10 ELSE GOTO 30
```
The number **53** in line 30 may look odd. The number in address 65120 is made up from the output bit 5 and the input setting. When both switches are pressed the total is 48 + 5 = 53.
You could use the 'logical AND' to make a 'mask' which looks only at lines 16 and 32 (= 48), try:
```
30 IF (?65120 AND 48)=48 THEN ?65120=10 ELSE GOTO 30
```
Having done this, the output settings don't affect the decision. (Chapter 9, page 150 has more detail about the 'bitwise logical AND'.)

Activity 7.6

Program to stop a buggy falling off a table top.

Assume that the left hand sensor is connected to line 16 and the right hand one to 32. When a feeler moves over the edge of the table the switch setting changes (fig 7.17)
For this argument, the motors are controlled as follows:
Forward 5, Reverse 10, Right 6, Left 9
Procedure calls make it easy to separate out sections of your program and treat them as an entity. This is really applying the systems approach to programming. The procedure becomes a **'component'** or a **'subsystem'** of the overall system. You will find it very helpful when your programs get complex.

Other computers use GOSUB routines. Indeed, you can use GOSUB on the BBC. However, in more advanced applications, a PROC is rather more versatile in the way in which it handles variables.

The PROC is defined from line 90 and completed at line 140.

```
10 ?65120=15
20 REM
```
(make red key f0 to stop buggy after escaping from program)
```
30 *KEY0 ?65120=0 M
```
(The symbol on the screen is obtained using the key marked to the right of and below the BREAK key)
```
40 ?65120=5: REM
```
(forwards)
```
50 X=?65120
60 PROCtest
70 GOTO 50
80
```
(You get this blank line by putting a SPACEBAR into line 80)
```
90 DEF PROCtest
100 IF (X AND 48)=48 THEN ?65120=10:I=INKEY (100):
     ?65120=6:I=INKEY (100):GOTO 130: REM (back off and turn right
     for set time)
110 IF (X AND 32)=32 THEN ?65120=9:I=INKEY (100): REM (turn
     left for set time)
120 IF (X AND 16)=16 THEN ?65120=6:I=INKEY (100: REM (turn
     right for set time)
130 ?65120=5: REM forwards
140 ENDPROC
```

Notes on the program

1 Line 30 sets up red key f0 to give an emergency stop when the program isn't running.
2 Line 80 is made a blank to mark where the procedure begins.
3 Procedure calls are always defined outside the main program. You start with DEF PROC . . . and finish with ENDPROC.
4 The logical AND acts as a mask to test a single bit.
5 I=INKEY (100) is a way of getting a delay of 100 1/100ths of a second. INKEY(T) waits for T 1/100ths of a second for a key to be pressed on the keyboard. If nothing happens, the program moves on. If a key is pressed, I takes the ASCII value of the key. (ASCII means American Standard Code for Information Interchange. It is a code for representing characters.)
6 Note that the test for both 'feelers' being active (48) comes first. If this is satisfied the buggy backs away from the edge and turns. The program then jumps to line 130 and the other tests (for 16 and 32) are not made. Each of them would also be satisfied but you don't want any further action taken on that basis.

8 Analogue inputs

Introduction

This chapter deals with the analogue input port and gives some practical examples of its use.

There are two ways of presenting electronic information, in digital or analogue form. **Digital** means one thing or another, with nothing in between. Digital watches and clocks give time to the nearest minute or second. They jump from one minute, or second, to the next, with no between stage. In digital electric circuits, only two states are allowed, ON or OFF, depending on whether the voltage is above or below a critical value (fig 8.1). You have seen that transistors, Darlingtons and logic gates behave in this way, they are either on or off.

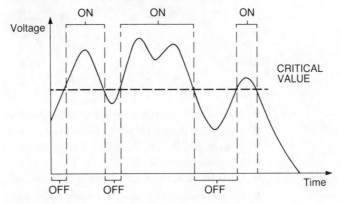

Figure 8.1

The BBC user port also works with digital information. Each line can take only one of two values.

Analogue means small variations (fig 8.2). Analogue watches and clocks have hands which sweep round and show gradual changes in the time rather than large jumps, from one minute to the next.

The BBC analogue port is at the back of the computer. It can measure any voltage between 0 and 1.8 V.

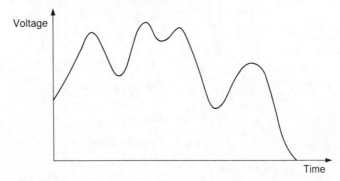

Figure 8.2

Connecting to the analogue port

The BBC computer has four analogue input channels which are connected through a 15-way D plug. There is also an earth, +5 V supply and +1.8 V reference. (The reference gives a steady voltage for accurate measurements. It does, however, vary very slightly as the machine warms up.)

You will need a way of making connections. Here are two suggestions for a low cost connection board. The 10 K resistors incorporated into the board offer some limited protection against accidental misconnection when the system is in use.

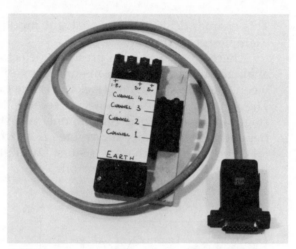

Figure 8.3

Design 1 (fig 8.3)

You need:
- 1 15-way D connector plug (RS 466-185) approx. £2
- 1 D plug cover (RS 469-572) approx. £1.5
- 1 terminal block, 12 way, 4 mm diameter barrel (RS 423-554)
- 1 wood base block 7 cm × 11 cm (thickness as appropriate)
- Length of wire with 7 lines approx. 80 cm long
- 4 10 K resistors (small enough to be incorporated into the D connector cover)
- Optional – 2 100 mA fuses in holder to be incorporated into +5 V and +1.8 V lines (e.g. RS 238-256/412-677)

Connections to the 15-way D connector need soldering, as shown in fig 8.4. This is the rear view. The 10 K resistors can be enclosed in the case.

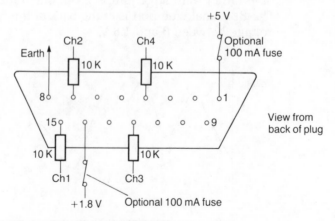

Figure 8.4

Connections to plug

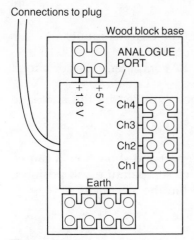

Figure 8.5

Design 2

Barrel terminal blocks are used at the other end of the lines. These are glue-gunned onto the base fig 8.5.

The rather tedious soldering of the connections to the D connector. Using design 1 can be avoided by using a ribbon cable squeezed into a speedblock connector. The other end is connected to a homemade pcb via a 16-way connector. See fig 8.6.

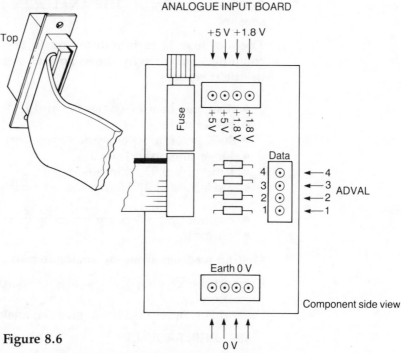

Figure 8.6

The layout for the pcb is shown in fig 8.7.
You need:
- speedblock D connector (RS472-629)
- 0.5 m 15-way cable (RS360-223 or can be made by stripping wires off from 20-way cable).
- pcb 16 pin connector (one pin unused) (RS471-373)
- pcb mounted fuse holder (RS413-147) optional
- 1 A 20 mm fuse (RS413-967) optional
- blank pcb 55 mm × 90 mm approx (RS435-484)

Refer to Chapter 6 page 101 for details about making a pcb.
Construct the board as shown in fig 8.6.
There are some points to watch:
1 Take special care to attach the plug to the cable in the right way.
2 Make sure that the cable is connected to the pcb connector leaving the unconnected pins in the right place.
3 Complete the cable connection **before** soldering the other pcb components.

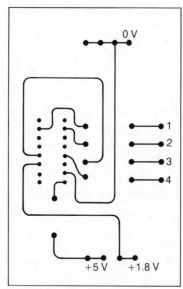

Underside view i.e. copper side

Figure 8.7

Warnings about using the analogue board

Do not connect a voltage greater than 5 V to the channel inputs.
Do not connect negative voltages to the input channels.
These could burn out the analogue chip in the computer. It is not a total disaster but it costs a few pounds to replace.
The investigations which follow use voltages supplied by the analogue port so there should not be any problems.

Practical activities

Activities 8.1 and 8.2 introduce the analogue port and show how it can be used to measure voltage difference, light level, temperature and position. A number of practical problems are included in the activities.

Activity 8.1

INTRODUCTION TO THE ANALOGUE PORT: using light sensors

The aim here is to introduce you to the analogue port on the BBC computer. This activity shows how to measure voltage and goes on to use light sensors.
You need:
  • analogue board (see figs 8.5 and 8.6)
  • dc voltmeter (5 V)
  • 10 K potentiometer (variable resistor)
  • ldr or phototransistor
  • lamp (6 V 0.03 A) in holder
  • a selection of different coloured cards (e.g. black, red, yellow, blue, etc)
  • 5 connecting wires e.g. croc clip connectors
  • plasticine

Getting readings from the analogue port

Connect the 'D' plug of the analogue board to the socket at the back of the computer.
Write this simple program to give the analogue port reading.

    10   PRINT ADVAL1

    20   GOTO 10

(ADVAL means Analogue to Digital Value)
Run your program.
You should see a random variation in the ADVAL number.
Connect channel 1 to earth. You should have 0 down the screen. In practice it won't be quite 0 but show a random fluctuation between 0 and 64.
Connect channel 1 to +5 V (or +1.8 V). You should have 65520.
You can get a number between 0 and 65520 depending on the voltage level of the channel 1 input.
The number is in proportion to the voltage level.
    0 V gives 0
    0.9 V gives 32760 (65520/2)
    1.8 V gives 65520
    greater than 1.8 V gives 65520
To use the other channels type ADVAL2, ADVAL3 and ADVAL4.

Activity 8.1 continued

The computer as a voltmeter

Check that you can get the computer to measure voltages up to 1.8 V. Connect the 10 K potentiometer (variable resistor) so as to divide the +5 V supply. Make this 'divided' voltage level the input to channel 1. Connect the voltmeter to measure this level. See fig 8.8.

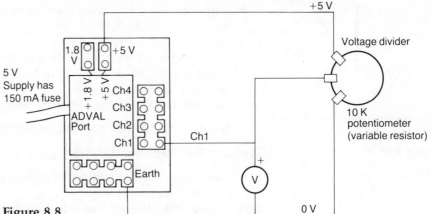

Figure 8.8

Run the program.

Compare the screen value with the voltmeter reading as you change the voltage divider setting.

To calculate the voltage level divide the 'ADVAL' reading by 65520 and multiply by 1.8.

Change line 10 to become:

```
10   PRINT (ADVAL1/65520)*1.8
```

Does it work?

[To limit your answer to 2 decimal places, add line 5 as follows:

```
5    @%=&20202
```
 (See the BBC User Guide under 'PRINT' for the explanation)

You should find that the computer will not measure voltages greater than 1.8 V.

Check that you can use the other channels.

Some practical problems

- Can you solve these problems dealing with light sensors?

Problem 1 – Using a light sensor

- Can you show when the brightness of light falling on a sensor (ldr or phototransistor) exceeds a set level?

Hint: Use a voltage divider circuit and the connections shown in fig 8.9.

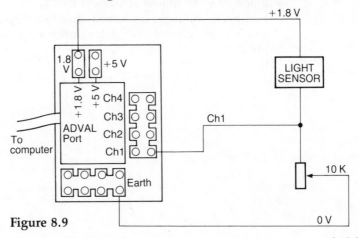

Figure 8.9

Activity 8.1 continued

- What happens if you exchange the positions of the sensor and variable resistor?
- Does the response seem linear? In other words, if the light becomes twice as bright, does the reading change by a factor of two?

Problem 2 – Identifying colour

- Can you make the computer identify colour by testing reflected light? Look at fig 8.10.

In making the system reliable consider:

Should the incident light always have the same brightness?

Should the sensor be placed to collect light which is 'reflected' according to the laws of reflection?

You may find the following structure helpful in your program:

IF ADVAL1>50000 AND ADVAL1<51000 THEN PRINT"RED"

Problem 3 – Graphing light changes

- Can you make the computer draw a graph to show how the light level changes with time?

This is quite difficult as you need to work with BASIC and BBC graphics.

Two program solutions are given below which you can use as models.

I suggest that you convince yourself of the meaning of each line by making changes and seeing what happens.

Drawing a graph (first way)

The main problem is getting the readings to fit the screen. This is divided into 1024 vertical units and 1280 horizontal ones. See fig 8.11.

Start by making the vertical readings ADVAL1/65. This should give you values 0–1000.

The command DRAW X, Y will draw a line from the last named point to the co-ordinates X, Y.

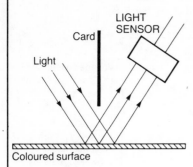

Figure 8.10

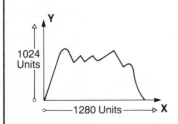

Figure 8.11

10	MODE0	(sets up mode for high resolution graphics)
20	FOR N=1 TO 1280	(the horizontal axis has 1280 units)
30	DRAW N,ADVAL1/65	(plots ADVAL readings on vertical axis moving across screen as N increases)
40	FOR X=1 TO 50:NEXT X	(time delay to slow up readings)
50	NEXT N	

Try changing the delay in line 40

If your programming experience is strong, you may be interested in a technique which collects data as quickly as possible and then plots a graph, e.g. to follow striking a match.

However, you need a sensor with a fast response time. To follow striking a match use a phototransistor. It responds much more quickly than the ldr.

Activity 8.1 continued

Drawing a graph (second way, fast collection of data)

```
10   DIM ARRAY%(1200)   (sets up an integer array with 1201 places)
20   *FX16,1            (sets the computer to look at Channel 1
                        only – others not used. Speeds up data
                        collection. See page 136).
30   FOR N%=0 TO 1200
40   ARRAY%(N%)=ADVAL1
50   NEXT               (faster if you omit the N%)
60   MODE0
70   FOR N%=0 TO 1200   (% means integer and is a faster proce-
                        dure)
80   DRAW N%,ARRAY%(N%)/65
90   NEXT N%
```

If your vertical scale is unsatisfactory, change the '65' in line 80.

Activity 8.2

USING THE ANALOGUE PORT: measuring temperature and position

You have seen that the analogue port measures voltage level. You can measure other quantities such as light level and temperature providing that you can convert them to a voltage level. **The aim of this activity is to introduce you to ways of measuring temperature and position.** You need:
- analogue board
- 10 K variable resistor ('pot')
- thermistor
- silicon diode or silicon temperature sensor
- hot water, thermometer 0–100 °C
- 100 K resistor
- 5 connecting wires e.g. croc clip connectors

Activity 8.2 continued

Measuring temperature using a thermistor

● Can you indicate temperature change using a thermistor?
Thermistor resistance falls as temperature rises.
You can make the thermistor part of a voltage divider circuit.
Set up the circuit as shown in fig 8.12.

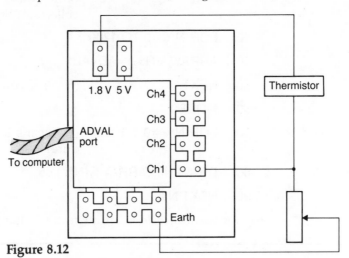

Figure 8.12

Does the reading increase or decrease as the temperature rises?
How is it different if you exchange the thermistor and variable resistor?
Are the readings proportional to temperature? i.e. if the temperature doubles, does the reading change by a factor of two?

Measuring temperature with a silicon diode

Can you measure temperature using a silicon diode?
Find a silicon diode and set up the circuit shown in fig 8.13.
Make sure the diode is connected in the orientation shown.
It responds linearly with temperature change.
Can you get readings which change with temperature?
A silicon diode can be used as an electronic thermometer. It's cheap but isn't very reliable. (At room temperature the voltage will be about 0.6 V. As temperature rises this will decrease by approximately 2.5 mV/°C)
You need two standard temperatures to calibrate it. Find the ADVAL readings at these two temperatures. Measure the temperatures with a standard thermometer.
Take the two standard temperatures as T1 and T2.*
These give ADVAL readings R1 and R2.
For an unknown temperature T, you get a reading R. You can work out T using:

$$T = \frac{(R - R1)\,{}^{*}(T2 = T1)}{(R2 - R1)} + T1$$

T = unknown temperature
R = reading for unknown temperature
T1 = first known temperature
R1 = reading at first known temperature
T2 = second known temperature
R2 = reading at second known temperature.
You can get the computer to do the calculation for you!
　　　*Purists will use the 'fixed points'. i.e. the temperature of pure melting ice =0 °C and the temperature of steam from pure boiling water =100 °C.

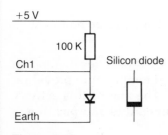

Figure 8.13

Activity 8.2 continued

Measuring position

Can you measure angle turned?
Connect up the voltage divider as shown in fig 8.14. Fix a pointer to the shaft (e.g. using a sticky label).

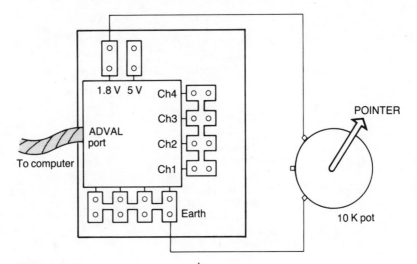

Figure 8.14

- Can you write a program which tells how many degrees the pointer has been turned from a reference position?

I suggest that you begin by turning the pointer fully anti-clockwise and make this the reference position. What is the change in the ADVAL reading when you turn the pointer through 180°?

- Can other angles be found by proportion?
  e.g. suppose 180° gives a change of 30000. For any other change, angle turned should be (change in reading/30000)*180
- Does it work?

Measuring height

- Can you measure the heights of three different blocks varying between 1 and 6 cm?

This is really an extension of the previous problem.
See fig 8.15. You can do it by trial and error. It is also possible to devise and use a 'trig' relationship (like sin, cos or tan).

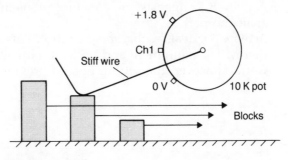

Figure 8.15

Activity 8.2 continued

Measuring weight

- Can you use a voltage divider to measure weight in the range 0–1 N (100 g wt)?

Two ideas for starters are given in fig 8.16.

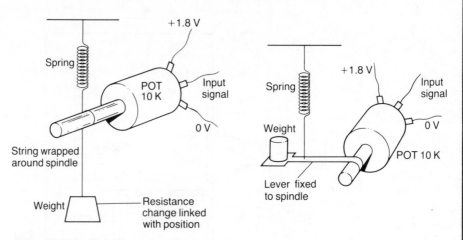

Figure 8.16

Time interval between analogue readings.

It takes a short time interval (10 milliseconds) for the analogue chip in the computer to work out the ADVAL value. So, if all four channels are active it takes 40 ms to produce a set of readings.

You can speed matters up by turning off the unused channels with a *FX16 command.

e.g. *FX16,1 enables channel 1 only and samples every 10 ms.

*FX16,2 enables channels 1 and 2, each will be sampled every 20 ms.

The analogue port works much more slowly than the user port. The digital data of the user port has only two states (on/off) and is rather simpler to use.

Further activities

Having some experience of using the analogue input port, you should now be ready to use it in some control situations.

Activity 8.3 suggests some control problems involving feedback into the analogue port.

Activity 8.4 deals with a servo-control. This is an important idea in control theroy. The equipment and principles involved are reasonably straightforward. However, the setting up and proving will require some time.

Activity 8.3

USING THE ANALOGUE PORT FOR CONTROL

Introduction

This activity suggests some control problems which can be solved by 'feedback' into the analogue port.
You need:
- user port buffer (e.g. Marjon)
- analogue board
- a variety of equipment according to the problem and its proposed solution (high current solid state switches, relays, Darlington)

The problems can be solved using the techniques already explored.
A word of warning! Take special care that the analogue channel inputs are never connected to negative voltages or receive voltages in excess of 5 V.

Illumination control

Can you switch a lamp on when the light level on a surface falls below a set value, and switch it off when the light level exceeds another set level?
In other words build a system which begins to maintain uniform illumination.

You need:
- an output control (user or printer part) to switch a lamp on and off
- lamp able to give reasonable light output and can be controlled using a relay or solid state switch.
- (The motor reverse box may be a suitable controller)

Temperature control

- Can you maintain a steady temperature?

There are two things you could do.
  a Switch on a heater when the temperature is below a set value.
  b Switch on a cooling fan when the temperature is above a set value.
You need to control two output lines and use relays or solid state switches. A small coil of resistance wire (10 cm 25 SWG manganium wire) connected to a low voltage supply (6/12 V) makes a good heater. Alternatively, use a 12 V high wattage supply. The cooling fan could be a propeller fixed onto a 5 V motor.

Buggy control

- Can you make a buggy follow a black (or white) line?

You may remember that when we considered making a buggy follow a white line in Chapter 7 (Activity 7.6) I suggested that you should delay until you know about the analogue input. You could use two separate light sensors. However, there is a clever arrangement using two ldrs. Connect them in series as shown in fig 8.17. The ldrs receive light reflected from the floor. If both sensors are above a white surface, the resistances are approximately equal and the reading should be around 32710 (65520/2).

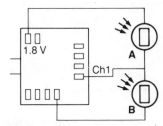

Figure 8.17

This will also be true if both sensors are over a dark surface. However, if one is dark and the other bright, then the balance will change.
Suppose A is dark and B bright. A will have the larger resistance. It will also have the larger voltage difference. So, the reading will fall well below 32710. The clever point is that this will work even when the ambient light changes.

- Can you use this method to make a buggy follow a line?

Activity 8.4

OPTIONAL. BUILDING A SERVO-CONTROL

Introduction

The servo is an important example of feedback control.

In a servo mechanism, you set a goal position. The system then moves towards this position. As it does so, information about the present position is fedback. In this way, the system 'knows' when it has reached the goal position.

It can be relatively easily and cheaply set up using the analogue and user ports. It is, however, an advanced challenge. The ideas are not particularly difficult. It is just that there are rather a lot of connections to make which will take some time.

You need:

- analogue port
- user port
- motor reverse board
- 2 10 K linear variable resistors ('pots')
- 5 V motor with rubber band drive
- 2 coffee jar lids
- connecting wires
- small base board and glue gun.

Can you build a system where the setting of the input pointer controls the position of a second pointer? See fig 8.18

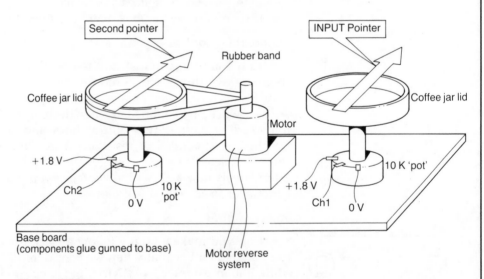

Figure 8.18

There are many connections to make. As far as possible, check that each is working as you connect it up.

Connect the voltage dividers across the 1.8 V supply and take the 'centre taps' to Channels 1 and 2.

Connect a user port so that port bits 1 & 2 switch the motor on/off and control its direction.

You can set the 'goal' position by turning the pointer on the input pot pointer. This is reported through ADVAL1. The position of the second pointer is found from ADVAL2. The difference is the 'error' and the motor should move the second pointer to reduce this error. Eventually, the second pointer should move to the same position as the input pointer and then stop.

Activity 8.4 continued

A specimen program

The program has been written to make the computer work as quickly as possible. It also uses **Procedure Calls**. These are short sets of instructions which are defined in sections beginning DEF PROC . . . placed at the end of the program. END PROC marks the end of the procedure.
PROCread finds the error in the positions. This is called X%.
PROCact (X%) acts on this value. This is an example showing how you can carry a variable into a procedure call. X% is an integer valued variable whose value depends on the different settings of the two potentiometers.
Z% is the error which you decide is acceptable before the system stops.

The motor turns the second pointer until the error, X% is less than Z%.
The blank lines are included to show the sections of the program. They are obtained by putting SPACEBAR into the line.
In setting up the servo it's useful to be able to look at the analogue readings. Lines 210, 220 do this.
You get into them by typing

　　GOTO210　RETURN

instead of RUN
To get out of the program press ESCAPE.

```
  10    *KEY0 ?65120= M
  20    REM SETS f0 KEY TO SWITCH ALL OUTPUTS OFF
  30    *FX16,2
  40    REM USE ONLY ADVAL CHANNELS 1&2
  50    Z%=3500:REM THIS SETS ERROR LIMIT
  60    ?65122=15:REM DATA DIRECTION REGISTER
  70
  80    PROCread
  90    PROCact(X%)
 100    GOTO 80
 110
 120    DEF PROCread
 130    X%=ADVAL1 − ADVAL2
 140    ENDPROC
 150
 160    DEF PROCact(X%)
 170    IF X%<=Z% AND X%>=−Z% THEN ?65120=0:ENDPROC
 180    IF X%>Z% THEN ?65120=1:ENDPROC
 190    IF X%<Z% THEN ?65120=2:ENDPROC
 200
 210    PRINT ADVAL1, ADVAL2
 220    GOTO 210
```

Activity 8.4 continued

The important points for fast response are:
Variables are made integer using the % sign.
Unused analogue channels are switched off using the *FX16 command.
Non-essential intermediate operations like PRINT have been eliminated.
As soon as an IF . . . THEN statement is satisfied, the shortest route out of the section is taken.

If your motor connections are the wrong way round, the motor will increase the error and the second pointer will move as far as it can away from the 'goal' position. This is 'positive' feedback. So, reverse the connections to get 'negative' feedback. i.e. the motor moves to reduce the error.
If the motor moves too quickly, it will overshoot the goal position. It will then return and may overshoot again. This is called **'hunting'** – it's hunting the target!

- Can you get the second pointer to move steadily to the goal position?
- What happens if you reduce the motor supply voltage?
- What happens if you change the value of the error setting Z% in line 50?

Procedure calls can help you to write well structured programs.
However, can the program be speeded up by doing without the PROCs?
The system can be developed to demonstrate some of the more advanced principles of control.

Summary

There are two ways of presenting electronic information, in digital or analogue form.
Digital means 'in steps'. Analogue means 'smooth change'.
The BBC can only really work with digital values. It converts a smooth change to a digital value using 'ADVAL' – analogue to Digital Value.
The computer can act as a voltmeter by using the analogue inputs.
The BBC has 4 channels each measuring up to 1.8 V.

Sensors can be used to measure a variety of quantities e.g. light level, temperature, position.
A sensor can be made part of a voltage divider circuit. The channel input is the 'divided' voltage.
The analogue ports can be used for control. They are slower acting than the user port because the digital information has only two states, on or off.

Consolidation questions

1 **A light sensor has been set up to detect colour as shown in figs 8.9 and 8.10**.
A program has been written which uses the ADVAL reading to test for a red surface. It works well and has been saved.
On setting up a second time, the program give spurious readings showing that something is wrong.

a) Which of the following could be a reason?
i The analogue port is not properly connected at the back of the computer.
ii There is a break in the voltage divider circuit containing the sensor.
iii The 'wrong' channel is being used.
iv There is no program running.
v The light sensor should be in the bottom arm of the voltage divider circuit.
vi A phototransistor sensor has been used instead of the ldr.
b Which of these could be checked using a voltmeter? What connections would you make?

2. **A thermistor has been set up to measure temperature as shown in fig 8.12. Two known temperatures have been used for calibration.**
The readings are:
Temp   ADVAL reading
20 °C   50000
40 °C   60000
What is the temperature for the following ADVAL readings?
(1)   55000
(2)   40000
It turns out that these don't precisely agree with an ordinary thermometer. Why not?

Solutions

Activity 8.2
Measuring temperature
using a thermistor

If the temperature rises, the resistance of the thermistor falls. The voltage at the junction of the two components will rise. The analogue port value with then rise. If the thermistor and variable resistor are exchanged, the analogue value will change in the opposite direction (i.e. will rise as the temperature falls). The readings do not change in a way which is directly proportional to the temperature change. The system is useful for indicating the way in which temperatures change. It is more difficult to measure temperature values on the Celsius scale.

Measuring position

You should find that the change in the ADVAL reading is directly related to the angle turned by the variable resistor ('pot').

Consolidation questions

1 (a) possible explanations are i to iii
iv If there is no program running, you wouldn't get a set of readings.
v and vi are possible explanations, but only if there have been changes since calibrating for the colour. The program could include a calibration for red, in which case, these alternative arrangements would work.
(b) Connect a voltmeter to give the Channel 1 input reading. This would help in sorting out i, ii and iii.

2 A 'linear' change is assumed.
Use the relation for temperature given in Activity 7.2
Alternatively, draw a graph.
i   30 °C
ii   10 °C
The two systems for measuring temperature are based on totally different principles. There is no reason why they should agree.

9 Filling some gaps

Introduction

This chapter deals with a number of important points which have not found a place under other headings. They are:

buffer board design
using numbers to represent data (binary and hex notation)
bitwise logical AND
TTL and CMOS chips
the common ground in linked circuits
practical ways of picking items up.

You have already been introduced to some of these. Others are new.

Marjon buffer board design

The Marjon board uses two 7400 chips which contain 4 two-input NAND gates. They act as **'fuses'**. If anything goes wrong with the connections to the buffer board, we hope that the chips will 'blow' rather than any components inside the computer. They also relate voltage levels to logic values in a convenient way. The 74LS00 chips are special low power chips which control a very small current. These are used for the input data to the computer.

Output lines

Each computer output line is connected to the input of a NAND gate. The NAND gate controls a load by 'sinking' the load current (fig 9.1).

The load could be a 6 V 0.06 A lamp, a reed relay switch or a single/double pole relay. NAND gates are not designed as current controllers and they cannot control any significant load current. Gates can also be used to 'source' current to a load, but they deliver much less current than they can sink (fig 9.2). This is, however, sufficient to act as a data signal, e.g. to switch a Darlington.

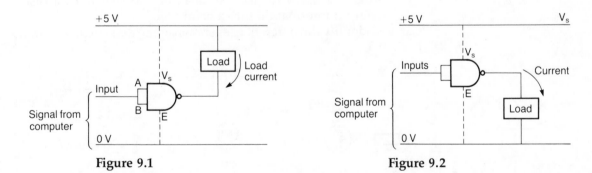

Figure 9.1   **Figure 9.2**

A light emitting diode (led) can be used to show when a computer output line is on. It is connected in series with a resistor which limits the current flow. See fig 9.3

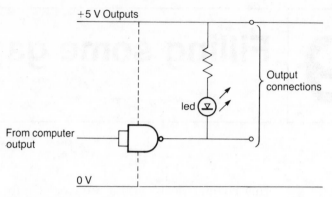

Figure 9.3

Input lines

Input lines to the computer also pass through a NAND gate (fig 9.4). The gate output is linked to the computer. As you know unconnected TTL inputs float high, so the standard input to the computer is 0.

The activity which follows is intended to draw together some of the points which have been made earlier and develop the theory behind the Marjon buffer board.

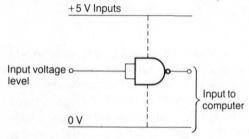

Figure 9.4

Activity 9.1

Consolidation questions on NAND gates as buffers
The aim of this activity is to consolidate some of the theory behind using NAND gates as buffers.
(For solutions see page 156 at the end of this chapter.)
   1 Generally speaking, you use electrical voltages for two purposes:
         To provide energy, e.g. to run a chip, lamp or motor.
         To give a signal for use as 'data', e.g. to switch a transistor or input information into a computer
   Can you identify the different uses shown in the four circuit diagrams in fig 9.5?

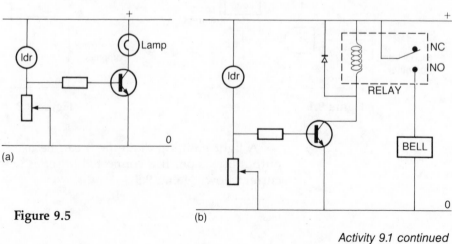

Figure 9.5

Activity 9.1 continued

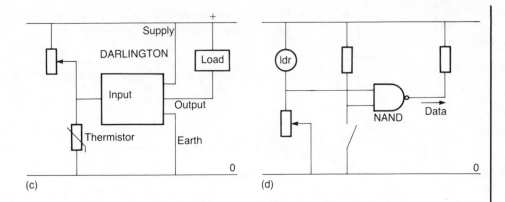

(c)   (d)

Figure 9.6

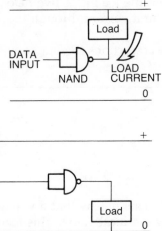

Figure 9.7

2 You can use a NAND gate to control a load (e.g. lamp or motor) by 'sinking' the load current.

  a What does 'sinking load current' mean?

  b There are two connections which are required to make a gate work which are not normally included on diagrams. They are not shown in fig 9.6. What are they?

  c What gate output will switch the load on?

  d If the two inputs to the gate are joined together, what input voltage will switch the load on?

3 Why don't we use NAND gates to source a load (fig 9.7)?

4 You are designing a buffer board for a computer output control. The computer output gives signal voltages of 0 V (off) or 2.5 V (on). These become inputs to a NAND gate which then controls the load. You have a 7400 chip which is a 'quad 2 input NAND'.

  a Complete a copy of fig 9.8 to show how you would make the connections for one output line. Remember that you need a voltage supply to run the chip.

  b Why do you need to link the earth to the computer?

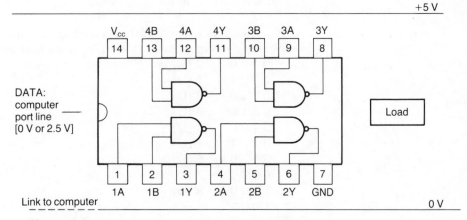

Figure 9.8

5 There are two inputs to a NAND gate. You only need one. The two inputs are usually linked together. However, there are other possibilities for the second input. These are:

  keep it at high voltage

  keep it at low voltage

  leave it unconnected.

• Which of these do the same thing as joining the two inputs together?

remember that unconnected TTL inputs float 'high' (TTL = transistor transistor logic).

6 When you have decided what to do with the second input (B) complete a logic table for the system.

Input A	Input Gate B	Output Z	Load on/off

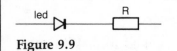

Figure 9.9

7 You also need a visual signal to show when the load is 'active'. Do this using an led with a series resistor to limit current through the diode (fig 9.9)
  • How will these be connected? Add these corrections to your copy of fig 9.8.

Using numbers to represent data

Binary notation

Computers work with two states, on and off. This means that a voltage at some place in the circuit is above or below a critical value. This leads to binary notation as a way of representing data, e.g. with 4 'bits of data.

0 0 0 1 means that the first three bits are off and the fourth is on.
The normal method of counting is in columns of hundreds, tens and units, e.g. 765 is

hundreds	tens	units
7	6	5

This system is known as the denary or decimal system.
There is a decimal equivalent (D) for each arrangement

0 0 0 0	0 (D)
0 0 0 1	1 (D)
0 0 1 0	2 (D)
0 0 1 1	3 (D)
0 1 0 0	4 (D)
0 1 0 1	5 (D)
0 1 1 0	6 (D)
0 1 1 1	7 (D)
1 0 0 0	8 (D)
1 0 0 1	9 (D)
1 0 1 0	10 (D)
1 0 1 1	11 (D)
1 1 0 0	12 (D)
1 1 0 1	13 (D)
1 1 1 0	14 (D)
1 1 1 1	15 (D)

There are 16 ways of combining the four '1's or '0's. If you expected it to be 15, remember that you have to count 0000 as one of the combinations.

The BBC is an 8 bit computer. This means that data is passed along eight lines. This give 16 × 16 combinations (= 256) and lets you count from 0 to 255. The data carried on the eight lines is called a byte of information.
In binary counting, 1111 1111 is 255 (D).

Hexadecimal notation

You could do all of the things in this book without knowing about hexadecimal notation. However, if you wish, you can use it instead of counting in the more normal base of 10 (denary system). Hexadecimal has a close link with binary. It is included here for those who want to prepare for further development.

Large binary numbers use lots of digits. For example, 1111 1111 1110 1110 is 65518 (D) and the BBC computer uses more than this number of memory locations. To make these large strings of digits easier to handle, the bits are grouped in sets of 4. Each set of 4 has 16 possible arrangements. A single character is used to represent each of these 16 arrangements. There is no problem from 0 to 9, but after this, letters ABCDEF are added. So, the count becomes:

Binary	Hexadecimal
0000	0
0001	1
0010	2
0011	3
0100	4
0101	5
0110	6
0111	7
1000	8
1001	9
1010	A
1011	B
1100	C
1101	D
1110	E
1111	F

This can be extended to two sets of four bits, e.g.

1111	0100, would be
F	8

and to four sets e.g.

0001	1000	1110	0000	would be
1	8	E	0	

This is equivalent to counting in columns of 16s. You normally count in columns of hundreds, tens and units in the denary or decimal notation. The system based on 16s is called hexadecimal.

Hexadecimal lets you 'concentrate' numbers into fewer columns. The great advantage is that there is an easy relation between 'hex' and binary numbers. Each pattern of four binary digits is associated with a hex number, e.g. 1010 is A. There is not, however, an easy relation between hex and denary/decimal.

If all this looks complex, look at the table below. It shows the different ways of counting.

Binary	Hexadecimal	Denary/decimal
0000	0	0
0001	1	1
0010	2	2
0011	3	3
0100	4	4
0101	5	5
0110	6	6
0111	7	7
1000	8	8
1001	9	9
1010	A	10
1011	B	11
1100	C	12
1101	D	13
1110	E	14
1111	F	15
1 0000	10	16
1 0001	11	17
1 0011	12	18
1 0100	13	19
1 0101	14	20

The pattern of voltage levels on the eight lines or 'bits' can be represented by a pattern of '0's and '1's. Each pattern is labelled by a hex or denary number.

Converting between the systems

In denary/decimal you have columns of hundreds, tens and units (i.e. 10^2, 10^1, 10^0).

In binary your columns are 8, 4, 2, 1 (i.e. 2^3, 2^2, 2^1, 2^0)

In hexadecimal you have 4096, 256, 16, 1 (i.e. 16^3 16^2, 16^1, 16^0). In hex you change columns when 15 is reached.

Consider HEX FE60

The first column represents blocks of 4096. There are 'F' of them. In denary F becomes 15. The second column represents blocks of 256. There are 'E' of them. In denary E is 14. The third column represents blocks of 16. There are 6 of them. The fourth column represents the single units, counting up to 15.

So Hex FE60 is

$15 \times 4096 + 14 \times 256 + 6 \times 16 + 0 \times 1 = 65120$

- Can you convert the following examples from binary into hex? For the answers see page 157
  0001 0001 0001 0010 is hex....
  1000 0000 0000 0010 is hex....
  1000 0000 0010 0010 is hex....
  1000 0000 1111 0010 is hex....
  1000 0000 1111 1100 is hex....
- Can you see how hex represents in blocks of four binary bits?

Activity 9.2

Consolidation questions on binary and hex
The aim of this activity is to practise some conversions between the different number systems.
You will need access to a BBC computer for questions 4 to 7. The answers are on page 00.
1 What is 0001 0011 1100 1111 in hex?
2 What is binary for hexFE62?
3 What is denary/decimal for hex001A?
4 For the BBC micro, the '&' sign is used to show that hex is being used, e.g. PRINT &1A gives the decimal value of hex1A. Try it. Check the answer to question 3.
5 To go the other way round and convert denary to hex, use the ' ' symbol (it's just below the BREAK key).
Try PRINT~65120 to give the hex equivalent. Note that on the screen the ~ appears as ÷.
6 Type
?20 = 10 then press RETURN
Remember that ? means the contents of address . . . (Yes, you can write into memory locations other than 65120!)
Memory location 20 will store the number 10. (This will really be a pattern of high and low voltages on a number of bits.)
You can check that this number has been stored in address 20 by typing PRINT ?20 then press RETURN
● Does it work?
● Now can you do the same thing using hex notation? Put a & in front of a number to show that you want it to be hex.
7 What is the largest number you can store in a given memory location, say address 200?
Give your result in denary and hex.
● What would it be in binary?
● Is it the same for another address?

Bitwise logical and -separating 'bit values' in a memory location

It is often useful to select out a single bit from the data in an address. You can use the 'logical AND' to do it. In fact this has already been suggested in Chapter 7.

Activity 9.3

Using the logical AND
This activity is aimed at showing how the logical AND works.
You need:
● BBC computer
Try some examples with a computer to see how the AND works. Write:
1   PRINT 1 AND 0 then press RETURN
2   PRINT 1 AND 1 then press RETURN
3   PRINT 2 AND 0 then press RETURN
4   PRINT 2 AND 2 then press RETURN
5   PRINT 2 AND 4 then press RETURN
6   PRINT 4 AND 4 then press RETURN
7   PRINT 5 AND 4 then press RETURN

Activity 9.3 continued

You will probably find the results surprising. We all expect that 1 and 1 is 2!.
'AND' is not the same as adding!

The AND operation matches the binary bits in the two numbers. Can you work out what is happening? Compare your results with those on page 158. The computer converts the data to high/low voltage on 8 data lines. It then works with these.

Where is the logical AND useful?

The number stored in a particular address can be linked with voltage levels on the 8 bits or lines of the computer. Take the Marjon board as an example. The 4 input bits (128, 64, 32, 16) are set by the outside voltage levels. The 4 output bits (8, 4, 2, 1) are set by the computer. These combine to give you a single number between 0 and 255 in address 65120. This number – called a **byte** – shows the setting of each of the 8 bits, e.g. 18 (which is Hex12) would be 0 0 0 1 0 0 1 0. 0 is low voltage and 1 is high voltage.

Suppose you want to take action on a particular input setting. You could subtract the output data from the total in the address, but this can be quite difficult in complex programs.

An easier way is to use the 'logical AND'. This acts as a **mask** and lets you test a single bit, or a combination of bits.

Suppose you want to test the value of bit 16. If the voltage on bit 16 is high then your address will contain a 16 in its sum. If bit 16 is low, this 16 will be absent. Suppose also that you have also set bit 1 to high voltage. The working address will contain 17, i.e.:

128	64	32	16	8	4	2	1	Total (D)
0	0	0	1	0	0	0	1	17

Compare this with 16 using the logical AND. The result will show where two bits are both on.

128	64	32	16	8	4	2	1	Total (D)	
0	0	0	1	0	0	0	1	17	AND
0	0	0	1	0	0	0	0	16	
0	0	0	1	0	0	0	0	16	

The computer compares the values of each bit and returns a value when the AND condition is met. Otherwise it gives 0. It works in binary bits – 1 AND 1 gives 1, otherwise 0. This is called a 'bitwise' logical AND operation. The result is 16. Try this on a computer. Write PRINT 17 AND 16.

Suppose you wanted to test the values of bits 16 and 32, both of which were at high voltage. Assume that bits 2 and 4 are also set high. The address would then contain 54. You need to PRINT the contents of the address AND 48. This will give you a mask to look at bits 16 and 32 alone (fig 9.10).

128	64	32	16	8	4	2	1	Total	
0	0	1	1	0	1	1	0	54	AND
0	0	1	1	0	0	0	0	48	
0	0	1	1	0	0	0	0	48	

A mask

Figure 9.10

To do this in practice write ?8000 = 54 RETURN. This puts 54 in address 8000. It sets the bit pattern 0 0 1 1 0 1 1 0. Now type PRINT ?8000 AND 48 RETURN. The result shows whether bits 16 and 32 (= 48) are high.

Try the following. Check whether the result is what you expect. PRINT ?8000 AND 16, PRINT ?8000 AND 32, PRINT ?8000 AND 1, PRINT ?8000 AND 2, PRINT ?8000 AND 255.

A practical example

Plug a buffer board into the user port. Write a program to report when a particular input bit is activated. Run your program. Then activate a variety of input lines to see if it works.

My suggestion tests bit 128:

```
10 ?65122=15
20 PRINT ?65120,(?65120 AND 128)
30 IF (?65120 AND 128) = 128 THEN GOTO 40 ELSE GOTO 20
40 PRINT"128 ON"
50 END
```

The comma in line 20 introduces a space on the screen between the two numbers which are printed on the same line. Notice that the AND operation has been put inside brackets. Is this necessary?

Other logical operations

You can also use OR and EOR. While AND makes a mask to look at particular bit settings, EOR is useful for changing particular bit settings. EOR is an **'exclusive'** OR. It works like this:

A	B	Result
0	0	0
0	1	1
1	0	1
1	1	0

An OR combination would give a high voltage if A is high, or B is high or if both are high. EOR is different. If A and B are both high the result is low voltage. If you use it, it will result in a change in the selected bit setting. Try some examples:

1 ?8000= 1 then press RETURN
   ?8000= ?8000 EOR 1 then press RETURN
   PRINT ?8000 then press RETURN
   Repeat this sequence a few times.
2 Suppose an address has bit value 8 set high and you wish to change the setting on bit value 2. Do this using EOR 2, i.e. write:
   ?8000= 8 then press RETURN
   ?8000= ?8000 EOR 2 then press RETURN
   PRINT ?8000 then press RETURN
   Enter ?8000= ?8000 EOR 2 followed by PRINT ?8000 a few times.
   • Can you see how EOR can change a bit setting and leave the others unchanged?

An important final point

One last important point. It is sometimes essential to enclose logic operations in brackets, e.g.
    PRINT (?65120 AND 8).
If you do not use brackets the computer will not execute the logic operation. As it does no harm, I suggest you always use brackets.

TTL and CMOS

You may have heard of the two families of chips called TTL and CMOS. TTL chips (transistor-transistor logic) are cheap, robust and fast in operation. They require a smooth supply close to 5 V. (You can just about use a 4.5 V or 6 V battery). Unconnected inputs 'float high'.

CMOS stands for 'Complementary metal oxide semi-conductor' and refers to the way the chips are made. They work with a supply between 3 and 15 V. This type of chip is rather more expensive and rather slower acting than TTL. They do, however consume less power, taking micro amps rather than milliamps of TTL. Unused inputs must be tied to the positive or negative rail. CMOS can be damaged by stray static discharge and the chips are usually stored with their legs electrically shorted.

Equivalent circuits can usually be found in TTL and CMOS. The critical switching voltages are different and problems arise if you try to mix the logic families.

voltage	TTL	CMOS
high	2.4 to 5.5	$(0.7 \text{ to } 1)V_{DD}$
uncertain	0.4 to 2.4	$(0.3 \text{ to } 0.7)V_{DD}$
low	0 to 0.4	$(0 \text{ to } 0.3)V_{DD}$

V_{DD} is the positive supply voltage. CMOS switching levels vary with the supply voltage. TTL levels are fixed.

Common ground in linked circuits

Sooner or later you will run into problems with your ground/earth connections.

Electric switching depends on setting up a voltage difference. It makes best sense to reference all voltage levels to a common ground which runs right through your circuits, i.e. the computer, the external supply and all switching circuits should share the same earth/ground level. This is particularly important when you obtain low tension from mains powered supplies. These are referenced to the mains earth. So is the computer. If the two earths are at different levels, you will have problems!

It can sometimes be difficult to arrange a common earth using the Marjon or Chelt-out buffers. This is when they are used to switch a load placed between the positive supply and data output.

It looks as though a common positive supply is required. Unfortunately, this will lead you into all kinds of problems.

Ways out of the difficulty: The first method is to allow the solid state switches in the buffer to work relays, i.e. reed relay, or single or double pole relays (fig 9.11). The circuit which is controlled by the relay is electrically independent of the solid state switch, so the controlled circuit can be linked to the common earth. It can also have a different supply voltage.

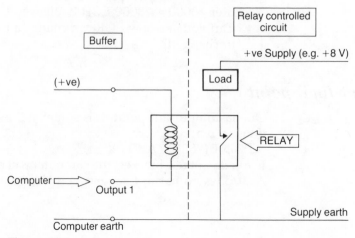

Figure 9.11

An alternative way is to take the output from the buffer and use it as 'data' (fig 9.12). Data carries very little current but can switch other solid state systems, e.g. the solid state motor reverse board. This data is referenced to the common ground.

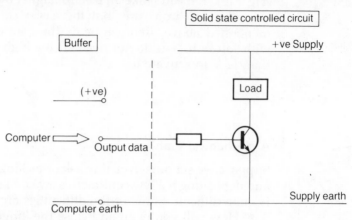

Figure 9.12

Picking up or separating things

In control applications, you often want to pick things up or separate things out. This section deals with some practical ways of doing it.

Pushing things aside

Suppose you have a conveyor belt and want to separate some of the items on it. Movement of items can be produced using the magnetic effect of an electric current. So, it may be possible to use an electric motor or solenoid.

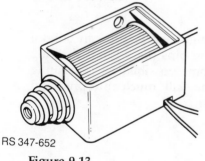

Miniature solenoid

RS 347-652

Figure 9.13

A miniature solenoid is useful for thrust or pull action. Small ones are used to activate points on model railways. RS have a useful 12 V solenoid for around £3 (RS 347–652). See fig 9.13. Its plunger moves 1.2 cm which is enough to kick small objects off a conveyor belt. However, it does need a high current – up to 4 A, but fortunately only in short bursts. This solenoid can produce forces in excess of 0.5 N. Take special care not to leave it on carrying a high current. If you do, it will get hot, but more importantly, you may well burn out your control circuit, especially if you are running it at above its continuous current limit.

Controlling the solenoid

1 An octal Darlington chip will work the solenoid providing you share the current between the Darlingtons, each can sink up to 0.5 A. However, if you accidentally leave it switched on, the current may burn out the chip.
2 The best solution is to use a high power transistor, e.g. TIP 2955, fig 9.14. This will sink current of many amps. If it runs hot in your application add a 'clip-on' heat sink. The solenoid can also be used to move barriers for separating items (fig 9.15).

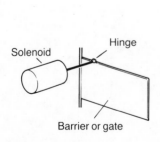

Figure 9.14

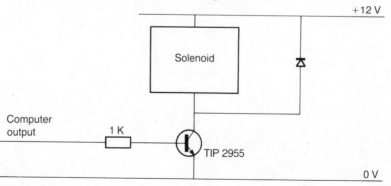

Figure 9.15

Picking things up

Figure 9.16

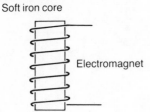

Soft iron core

Electromagnet

The magnetic solution

The easiest way is to use an electromagnet to pick up something magnetic! (Fig 9.16). You can make an electromagnet by winding many turns of wire around a soft iron core, but the easier solution is to use the solenoid mentioned above. Remove or fix the core of the solenoid, or replace it with soft iron. You do not need such a high current as before, so use less than 12 V to activate it.

Figure 9.17

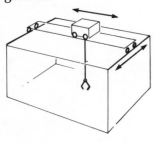

Robot arm

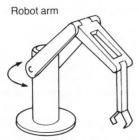

Figure 9.18

A mechanical grab?

Suppose we set ourselves the task of picking up an Oxo cube at one point and depositing it a few centimetres away. Making a 'hand' to grip the cube is quite difficult. Some of the difficulties are:

- How will you open and close the 'fingers'?
- How will you make sure the grip is not too strong yet sufficiently so to hold the cube?

There is also the problem of getting the 'hand' to the right places. An overhead gantry is an easier solution (fig 9.17). Even so you will quickly need more than four output lines.

If you are contemplating making a robot arm (fig 9.18) you are making life very difficult for yourself. The joints must be reliable and you need to be able to move them in each direction.

Designing a hand

It is best first to see how the mechanism might work. You can build a prototype from card and joint it with drawing pins (fig 9.19). A drawing board base is helpful. The diagrams show some possibilities. Translating the prototype to a working model needs some skill, much enterprise and a significant amount of time.

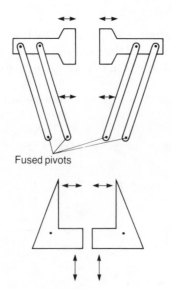

Fused pivots

Figure 9.19

A snake arm?

There is quite a nice idea sometimes used in industry, which controls an arm with wires (fig 9.20). I have never seen a homemade one but you might like to know the principle.

The mechanical problems in making a mechanical grab are a considerable challenge. Don't undertake them lightly. You may be able to adapt some system already constructed, such as a technical toy.

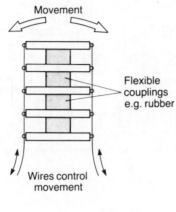

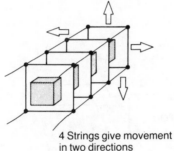

4 Strings give movement
in two directions

Figure 9.20

Summary

Voltage differences do two things. They provide:
　　　　energy or
　　　　data/information

In computing/electronics, three counting systems are used: binary, denary/decimal and hexadecimal.
Binary shows the voltage levels on each of the lines associated with an address. Denary and Hex describe this arrangement of voltage levels in 8 lines.
The bitwise logical AND acts as a mask and separates out the value of particular bits.
There are two families of chips – TTL and CMOS.
They do the same things but have different switching voltage levers.
When linking circuits together, it is important to have a common ground/earth.
A solenoid is useful for picking things up.

Solutions

Activity 9.1

1 See fig 9.21. D = data; E = energy. The decisions are not always clear cut. You may argue differently from my solutions.

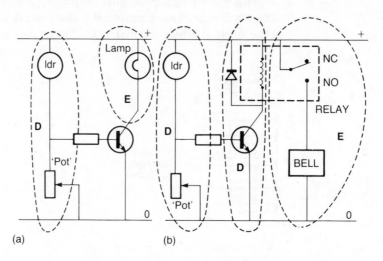

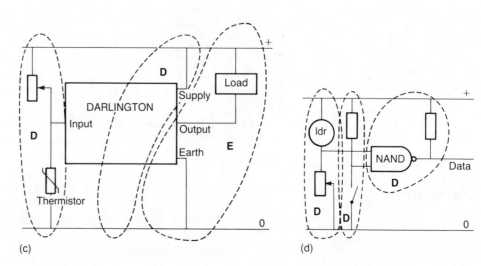

(a) (b)

(c) (d)

Figure 9.21

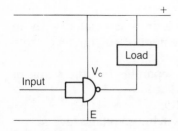

Figure 9.22

2 **a** 'Sinking' means that the current passes from the positive supply through the load and then into the gate at its output connection. Current only flows when the gate ouput voltage is low.
   b The missing connections are the +ve supply to the gate and the earth connection (fig 9.22).
   c A low voltage at the output switches the load on. This sets up a large voltage difference across the load.
   d A high voltage at the input switches the load on. The NAND gate acts as voltage inverter.

3 Logic gates cannot supply any significant current to source a load.

4 (i) A possible circuit is shown in fig 9.23.

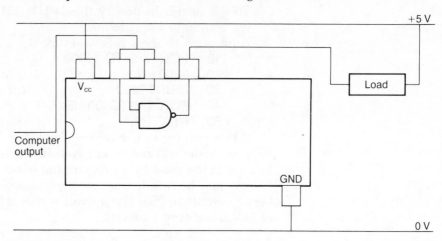

Figure 9.23

V_{cc} = +5 V to run chip
GND = earth connection to complete electrical circuit.
The computer line is connected to both inputs of NAND. (Consider alternatives later.)
The load is connected between +5 V and gate output. Current sinks into NAND gate output.

(ii) The earth must be linked to the computer to give a reference for the data voltage level.

5 Remember that a NAND gate is the inverse of AND. The key point is that you only get a low output when both inputs are high.
If one output (B) is held high you can get the gate to change by varying the other (A).
The gate will work if you:
    make B high or
    leave B unconnected (B will float high, but this is not recommended).
    (and also when you connect B to A).

Figure 9.24

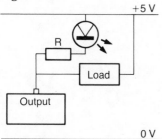

6

Input A	Input gate B	Output Z	Load on/off
0	0 or 1	1	off
1	1	0	on

7 The led and resistor should be connected in parallel with the load (fig 9.24). Check the diode polarity.

Converting between systems

0001 0001 0001 0010 is hex1112
1000 0000 0000 0010 is hex8002
1000 0000 0010 0010 is hex8022
1000 0000 1111 0010 is hex80F2
1000 0000 1111 1100 is hex80FA
Now can you see how hex represents blocks of four binary bits?

Activity 9.2

(1) 13CF
(2) 65122
(3) 31
(6) Write ?20=&A. PRINT ?20 will still give 10. PRINT ←?20 should give A. Alternatively, you could write ?&14=&A if you wanted to use hex for all numbers. PRINT ?20 should still give 10.

(7) The largest number which can be stored in address 200 should be 255. This is hexFF. In denary this is 1111 1111. All 8 bits (or lines) which the computer uses are on.

A program to show this would be:

```
10   FOR N=0 TO 10000
20   ?200=N              (puts N into address 200)
30   PRINT?200           (prints contents of address 200)
40   FOR T=1TO100:NEXT T (time delay)
50   NEXT N              (increases N by 1)
```

When you try to use different memory locations strange things may happen. Some will not accept your instructions. If you happen to pick a location being used by a program the result could be quite interesting!

You may be wondering how the computer manages to cope with numbers greater than 255. The answer is that it holds the number in a group of linked memory locations.

Activity 9.3

Each bit is compared. The result is 1 if both the first bit is 1 AND the second bit is 1. These are marked *. The result is 0 if either the first or second bit is 0 or both bits are 0.

1   1 AND 0
       0 0 0 1   (1)   (first bit)
       0 0 0 0   (0)   (second bit)
result   0 0 0 0   (0)

2   1 AND 1
       0 0 0 1   (1)
       0 0 0 1   (1)
result   0 0 0 1   (1)

3   2 AND 0
       0 0 1 0   (2)
       0 0 0 0   (0)
result   0 0 0 0   (0)

4   2 AND 2
       0 0 1 0   (2)
       0 0 1 0   (2)
result   0 0 1 0   (2)

5   2 AND 4
       0 0 1 0   (2)
       0 1 0 0   (4)
result   0 0 0 0   (0)

6   4 AND 4
       0 1 0 0   (4)
       0 1 0 0   (4)
result   0 1 0 0   (4)

7   5 AND 4
       0 1 0 1   (5)
       0 1 0 0   (4)
result   0 1 0 0   (4)

10 Sensors

Introduction

There are no practical activities in this chapter. It is intended to give you ideas for practical measurement. It lists some of the sensors available and indicates how they can be used. Some of these sensors have been discussed already in other chapters.

Electronic sensors can measure all kinds of things e.g. light level, temperature, position and force. Most are based on a change in resistance as the measured quantity of light, temperature, etc. changes. Sensors are sometimes called transducers (from Latin, trans=across, duce=lead). They 'lead' one kind of change 'across' to become an electrical change.

Kinds of sensors

There are essentially three kinds of sensors. Some are really switches e.g. microswitch, magnetic switch and tilt switch. Others depend on a change in their resistance e.g. light-dependent resistor (ldr), phototransistor and thermistor. The third kind generate a voltage difference. Examples of this type are thermocouples and piezo-electric force sensors. A thermocouple has two junctions of different metals e.g. iron and copper. The emf generated depends on the temperature difference between the two junctions (fig 10.1). When certain types of crystals are squashed, a voltage difference is developed between their faces. This is known as the piezo-electric effect. It is used in a crystal microphone and record player pick-up. Both the thermocouple and piezo-electric methods develop a very small emf. So an amplifier has to be used, making the method more complex. The use of amplifiers to increase the size of the emf produced is discussed later in this chapter.

There are many control applications which use the two simple sensor systems (switches and changes in resistance) and we will concentrate on these.

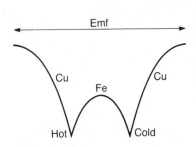

Figure 10.1

Simple systems

Switches

As you already know switches have two states – on and off. They can be connected to an input line to make it high or low voltage as in fig 10.2. The logic setting changes when the switch changes. In other words, they are digital. It is best to think of a switch as part of a voltage divider (potential divider) arrangement.

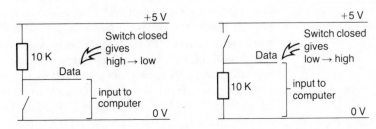

Figure 10.2

Resistance sensors

Sensors which change resistance slowly are really analogue devices. (They change gradually, not suddenly as switches do). Like switches, resistance sensors are also made part of a voltage divider system – as shown in fig 10.3. This allows their sensitivity to be changed by altering the resistance of the variable resistor.

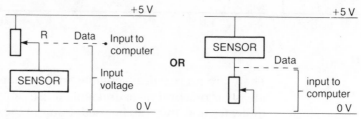

Figure 10.3

If you want digital information, the resistance can be adjusted to make the input voltage pass across the critical value as appropriate. This will change the logic state.

Resistance sensors can also be used as analogue input. The voltage level will change as the quantity being measured changes. However, care must be taken to make sure that the measured voltage lies within the appropriate range. This is 0 to 1.8 V on the BBC analogue input.

Examples of sensors

Switches

(a) Homemade switches – It's surprisingly easy to make your own switches using simple materials like paper clips, drawing pins and aluminium foil. An example of a homemade switch is shown in figure 10.4.

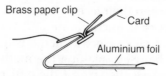

Figure 10.4

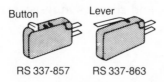

RS 337-857   RS 337-863

Figure 10.5

(b) Miniature microswitches (button and lever), fig 10.5

Lever switches are useful as bumpers to indicate when a position has been reached. The lever can be extended to make them easier to switch.

(c) Magnetic reed switch. These switch when a magnet is brought close by. As shown in fig 10.6 they consist of two pieces of soft iron attached at one end to springy metal, all enclosed in a glass case. Normally the soft iron is not magnetised but when a magnet is brought close to the switch the soft iron becomes magnetised. The end of the pieces of soft iron facing each other always become opposite poles and so attract each other and come together to complete the circuit. When the magnet is removed the soft iron pieces lose their magnetism and they spring apart breaking the circuit. Reed switches are used in intruder alarms, for example to indicate when a window or door has been opened. They only carry small currents, 200mA or so. Don't exceed the manufacture's rating. Another disadvantage is that they suffer from considerable switch bounce.

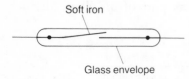

Figure 10.6

(d) Mercury position or tilt switch
Electrical contact is completed through liquid mercury enclosed within the container (fig 10.7). If the switch tilts, one of the contacts loses contact with the mercury and breaks the electric current. They are used to control the orientation of equipment and also in security systems.

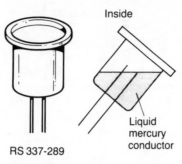

RS 337-289

Figure 10.7

Examples of analogue switches/transducers

Light sensors

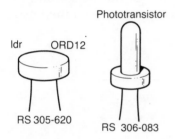

Figure 10.8

There are many kinds, ldrs and phototransistors are common examples of light sensors, see fig 10.8.

The ldr is relatively slow acting, taking a few hundred ms to respond to a light change. It's resistance falls to quite a low value (100 Ohm) as the light intensity falling on it increases.

The phototransistor is very fast acting and is most sensitive to the infra-red (heat) end of the light spectrum. Like the ldr, it's resistance falls as light increases but the values always remain very high, some kilohms. It must be connected the right way round.

Light sensors are often used to tell when a light beam has been interrupted. When the wheel rotates the beam of light passing through the hole is broken.

You can use reflected light to test whether the sensor is near to a surface, to indicate the colour of a surface or to detect movement of a wheel by the changes in the amount of light reflected from the wheel, as shown in fig 10.9.

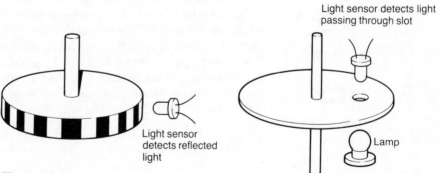

Figure 10.9

A switch with a built in logic circuit and infra-red source is useful for sensing position by detecting light reflected from a nearby surface. This type of switch is called a reflective opto switch, an example is shown in fig 10.10. In the switch illustrated there is an infra-red emitting led and a phototransistor sensor housed together in a single casing.

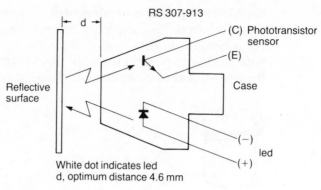

Figure 10.10

Temperature sensors

Thermistors

A thermistor is a quite common device which is used to indicate temperature so it is a type of thermometer. The resistance of a thermistor falls as its temperature rises, as shown in fig 10.11; this fall becomes increasingly rapid at higher temperatures. This makes it quite a challenge to measure temperatures over a wide range of values. Thermistors are cheap and available in a variety of shapes and resistance values. So you can choose one which suits your requirements, for both size of the sensor and the range of temperatures to be measured. Be careful to connect a thermistor in the way shown in fig 10.12.

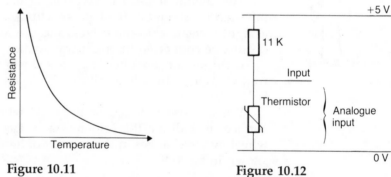

Figure 10.11   **Figure 10.12**

Two particular thermistors are recommended:
Siemens part K164-2.2K is available from Electrovalue Ltd, (see appendix) at about 20p each. This is suitable for general measurements of temperatures between 0 and 100 °C. Miniature bead RS 151-142 cost about £3. These are very sensitive and can be used to detect heat radiation.

There are other systems. If you are not too fussy about consistancy, any old **silicon diode** makes a good thermometer with a linear response. Take care to connect it in the way shown (fig 10.13).

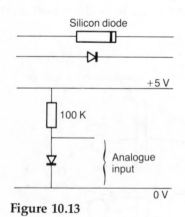

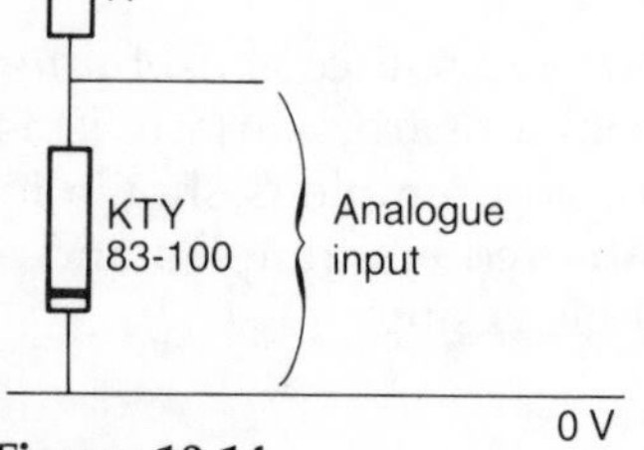

Figure 10.13

Figure 10.14

Silicon temperature sensors

Silicon temperature sensors are much better than thermistors. They are very linear and more reliable. A silicon sensor for example Mullard KTY83-100 measure temperatures over the range −55 to 175 °C. It costs around 45p. It should be used as shown in fig 10.14.

All of these temperature sensors are very suitable for control applications. They are cheap and simple to connect, as they use nothing more complex than a voltage divider circuit.

Other temperature sensors

It may be worth mentioning two other temperature measuring systems. These are rather more expensive and have been designed to produce a voltage change of 10 mV per °C. This makes it easy to measure temperature in °C. They can be linked directly to a voltmeter but, of course, could be linked to the analogue input of a computer.

The first is an **integrated circuit** ref. LM35. It requires a voltage difference (5 V is suitable). The output can be fed directly into the analogue port. (fig 10.15). There are two versions costing around £3 (0 to 100 °C) or £6 (−40 to 110 °C). The RS stock numbers are 317-954 and 317-960 and a data sheet can be obtained from RS giving full details of how to use them.

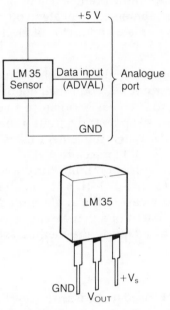

Figure 10.15

The second kind uses a thermocouple. It needs a thermocouple amplifier chip AD595AO (RS 301–779) costing around £7. The connections should be soldered on a chip socket as shown in fig 10.16 then the chip is plugged into the socket. The thermocouple wire is an additional expense. Thermocouple junctions have a very small thermal capacity (they require a very small amount of heat to change their temperature). This makes the thermometer fast acting, which is one of its major advantages. The thermocouple and amplifier chip also has a large range from 0 to 300°C.

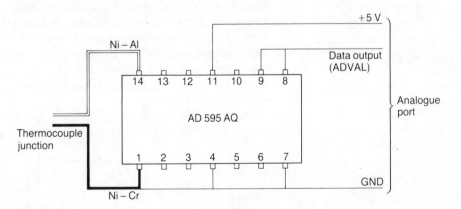

Figure 10.16

It is possible to make your own thermocouple by welding two wires of different metals to form the junction. You will need a high temperature flame, e.g. methane gas and oxygen, borax flux is suitable.

The BBC analogue port can be used as a thermometer. **Reminder –** ADVAL means Analogue to Digital Value. If you have forgotten about using the analogue port see Chapter 8, page 127. 1.8 V gives an ADVAL reading of 66520. These thermometers give a voltage difference of 10 mV per °C. Now 1 mV would give an ADVAL reading of 65520/1.8/100°

So 10 mV would give 10 × 65520/1.8 /1000 = 364

This represents a 1°C change.

The program to measure temperature is simple, e.g.

```
10 @=&20105: REM                    gives 1 decimal place
20 PRINT ADVALI/364" deg C"
30 GOTO 20
```

One final important point – if any of these thermometers described above are to be immersed in water you will have to provide electrical insulation, as water is a conductor of electricity.

Position Sensors

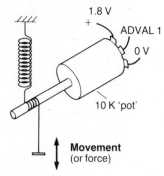

Figure 10.17

A lever microswitch or light sensor is useful to show arrival at a particular position but it cannot tell you much about what happens before arriving at the position. You can easily organise a voltage divider (pot) and spring to show position. Wrap a string around the spindle of a potentiometer as shown in fig 10.17. When movement takes place, the pot turns. This can be linked into a circuit to measure voltage. If you want to take this method seriously, use a low friction multi-turn potentiometer but they are expensive, at around £5. (RS 173–417). If you attach a lever to a voltage divider spindle, you can measure the angle turned by the lever, as shown in fig. 10.17b. The movement of a vehicle can also be detected by using a photo-transistor, such as adapting the methods shown in fig. 10.9.

Force measurement

Springs are widely used to measure forces. For example, you could measure the extension of a spring using a string wrapped around a potentiometer spindle (fig. 10.17a). This poses the same electrical problems as position measurement.

Strain gauges

These are used widely in industry to measure the minute changes in the shape of materials when forces are applied. A strain gauge is a thin film of metal foil stuck onto the surface of a material – usually metal (fig. 10.18). Large forces applied to the material stretch or compress it a small amount. This in turn stretches or compresses the foil and changes its resistance. It is important to realise that the stretch or compression is very small – too small to see by the naked eye. The change in electrical resistance is also very small. Very high amplification is needed to show any change. Precautions to eliminate effects due to temperature changes are also required. The system is reliable and usually gives a reading proportional to the force. A strain gauge suited to the particular metal being used is needed. Having said all this, I would not advise using strain gauges unless you are specially interested in them.

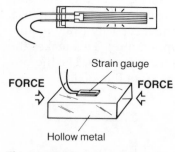

Figure 10.18

A differential amplifier circuit suitable for strain gauges is given in figs 10.19 and 10.20. This is definitely only for the enthusiast.

Pin functions
1 trimmer
2 −ve input
3 +ve input
4 earth (GND)
5 trimmer
6 output
7 +ve supply (V_{cc})

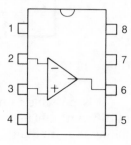

Figure 10.19

STRAIN GAUGE CIRCUIT

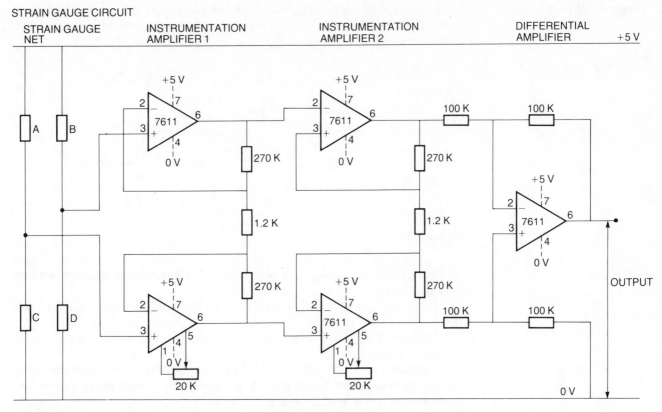

Figure 10.20

To make a **strain gauge amplifier** you need:
- 1 strain gauge
- 3 resistors equal to strain gauge resistance
- 5 7611 CMOS op-amp chips
  5 8-way sockets
- 4 100 K metal film resistors (0.4 W)
- 4 270 K metal film resistors (0.4 W)
- 2 1.2 K metal film resistors (0.4 W)
- 2 20 K 20-turn Cermet variable resistors
- stripboard 0.25 mm pitch

This is an advanced project. I leave you to plan the stripboard layout using fig 10.19. You could try using only one instrumentation amplifier.

The 7611 op-amp works well with only a +5 V supply. It has the same pin layout as a traditional op-amp such as the 741.

If you require a simple, cheap but very crude method to measure force, I suggest using carbon impregnated foam. (You sometimes find it around the legs of chips on delivery where it is used to prevent static discharge.) The foam has a high resistance which is reduced as it is squashed. However, it is not very elastic and takes a long time to recover and, your readings will not be very reliable. Try squashing some of this foam inside a syringe (fig 10.21a). Unfortunately, firms producing the foam only sell it in large quantities, so find someone who can give you a piece. A circuit using some carbon foam sandwiched between two coins is shown in fig 10.21(b).

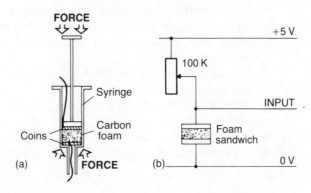

Figure 10.21   (a)   (b)

Water level indicators

These are easily built using two bare wires. When the water level rises and touches both wires or the wires are uncovered when the water level falls, the resistance change triggers a transistor (fig 10.22).

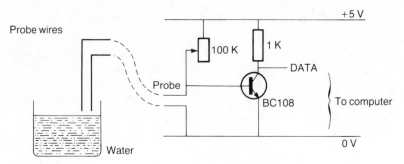

Figure 10.22

Conclusion

The list of sensors is not exhaustive but will allow you to do quite a lot in practical control.

There are others which I leave you to investigate when you find the need. These may include:

Magnetic pick-up (RS 304–166). This detects when a magnetic material is moved close by.

Pressure measurer (LX0503A). This is a solid state pressure transducer which measures between 0 and atmospheric pressure. It needs an instrumentation amplifier and must be kept dry.

pH probe (RS 424–557) is expensive and needs an operational amplifier.

Ultra-sonic transducers (RS 307–351, 307–367) can be used for remote control.

Summary

Electronic sensors can be used to detect a wide variety of things, e.g. temperature, light, position, force.
They are called transducers. They 'transduce' physical changes into electrical signals.
The two kinds of sensor which can easily be built into voltage divider circuits are switches and those which change resistance.
When using analogue sensors as part of a voltage divider system, the output voltage can be adjusted by using a variable resistor.

Consolidation questions on sensor applications

1 A buggy is to be run under computer control. You need a system which will report when a particular position has been reached.
   • List as many different ways of doing it as you can.
   • What are the advantages/disadvantages of each?
2 You are designing a lift to operate between four floors.
   • What sensors would you use to find out which floor the lift has reached?
   • Devise at least two methods of doing it. Which would you prefer to use in practice? Why?
3 Suppose that you have a horizontal table which must not be tilted at an angle greater than 10°.
   • Devise a 'homemade' way of sensing the angle.
   • Suggest at least one other way of doing it.

Solutions

Consolidation questions

1 The buggy position can be reported by a change in a sensor setting. Some suggestions are:
- light sensor carried by buggy affected by white card on floor
- fixed light sensor changes setting when buggy is close by
- fixed magnetic reed switch affected by magnet carried by buggy
- fixed microswitch changes setting when buggy makes contact
- homemade aluminium foil switch fixed to floor changes setting when buggy wheels pass over it

Other possibilities are:
- count the number of revolutions of the wheels using a light sensor carried by the buggy
- pull a piece of string wound round the spindle of a variable resistor (pot). Multi-turn pots are available.
- buggy trails a wiper which makes electric contact with aluminium foil stuck to floor

  In deciding the relative merits you might consider:
  reliability, cost, availability, ease of use, potential for further development/adaptation.

2 Some ways of testing the position of a lift are given in Chapter 12, page 181.

3 The tilt of a table could be reported using a lever. The end of the lever could make electrical contact with a metal ring when the tilt is greater than 10°.

You could also use mercury tilt switches. You would probably need more than one.

The platform could be pivoted on the axle of a variable resistor. The angle turned could be detected through the analogue port.

11 Stepper motors

Introduction

This chapter deals with stepper motors. They are much more expensive than ordinary motors but can be used to give very precise control of position. You would normally use a special chip to drive them, which again, adds to the expense. We will see how to run them. Details of how to make stepper motor control boards are also included in this chapter.

What is a stepper motor?

Figure 11.1

As you would expect from the name, the motor turns in a series of small steps. One step could easily be less than two degrees. It depends on the construction of the motor. Stepper motors are usually fatter than ordinary motors and have connections for several wires (fig 11.1). The wires are linked to field units. A typical stepper motor has four sets of field coils positioned round the rotor. These are energised one after the other (fig 11.2). The rotor is permanently magnetised and moves round in small steps following the magnetic field. (The 'rotor' is the part which rotates.)

Figure 11.2

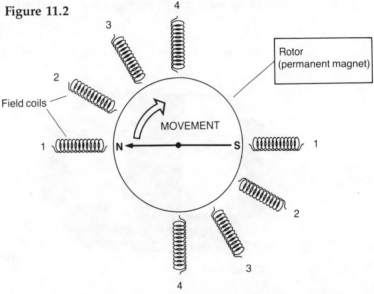

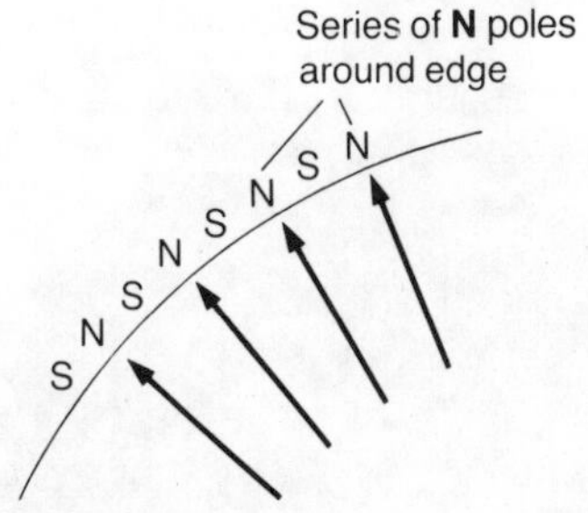

Figure 11.2 is a simplified diagram showing how this could be arranged. The coil arrangement is repeated to keep the rotor moving round. In the diagram the steps are about 30° apart. In a real motor they are much closer than this. In practice each field coil gives rise to a series of positions around the rotor where the magnetic field is high. There is also a series of permanent north poles around the edge of the rotor which corresponds to these positions (fig 11.3).

By changing the order of energising the coils, the motor can be made to turn forwards or backwards. The great advantage of stepper motors is that they give very accurate control of position. When linked through reduction gearing, it means that very precise positioning can be obtained. You find them in plotters and printers.

The speed of the motor can also be easily controlled. It depends on how quickly the field coil currents are changed. However, the system requires a lot of 'data'. The coils have to be activated in the right sequence.

Series of **N** poles around edge

Figure 11.3

Driving a stepper motor

You can run a stepper motor from a computer in two ways:

Method 1

The field coils can be controlled directly from the computer user port. It would need four lines and a special program to drive them in the right order.

Method 2

More conveniently you can use a special chip to control a stepper motor – this is the SAA 1027 chip. The coils of the motor are connected to this chip. It organises the logic to switch the motor coils on and off in the right sequence. This chip does not need to get this information from the computer, so it needs only two data lines from the computer – one line to trigger each step, one line to reverse the motor by changing the sequence of energising the coils.

These two data lines are the key inputs into the chip. One of these data inputs acts as the pulse trigger (pin 15); this activates the next set of coils when the input goes from high to low. The other data input controls the direction of the motor (pin 3); the direction depends on whether the input is high or low.

Use method 1 if you want to find out more about how a stepper motor works or if you do not have a control chip board. Otherwise use method 2.

Method 1 requires a user port buffer board (Marjon) and a Darlington chip.

Method 2 needs some kind of special arrangement to make connections to the SAA 1027 chip. You could use a breadboard. However, a more robust solution is to build a circuit on stripboard. This is described on page 172. You can also buy printed circuit boards. Marjon supplies one for a single motor with a voltage regulator included. NESTEC supplies one to control up to three stepper motors but without a voltage regulator. Made up versions are shown in figs 11.4 and 11.5. Maplin sells a kit for these chip circuits which also includes the motor. A circuit diagram is shown in fig 11.6.

Figure 11.4

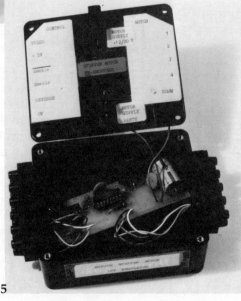

Figure 11.5

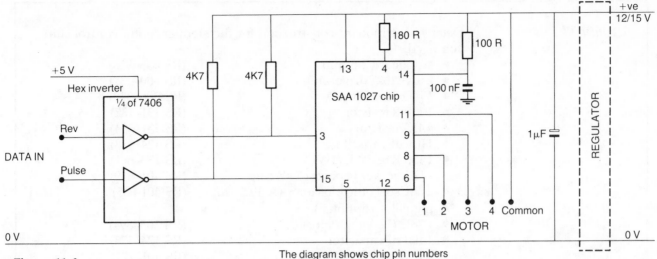

The diagram shows chip pin numbers

Figure 11.6

The circuit

The SAA 1027 chip uses input voltage levels which are different from those of normal TTL chips. High is above 7.5 V and low is below 4.5 V. These levels are obtained by using a hex inverter 7406 as shown in fig 11.7. This is an open collector chip. It allows us to obtain the required voltage levels by selecting an appropriate 'load' resistor connected to a 12/15 V +ve supply. 4K7 seems to do the trick. (As the gates are inverters, a low voltage results in a high voltage output. If you do not want such an inversion, substitute a hex buffer 7407 for the 7406. These gates have no inversions but keep the same connections.)

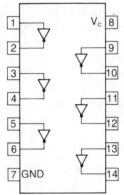

Figure 11.7

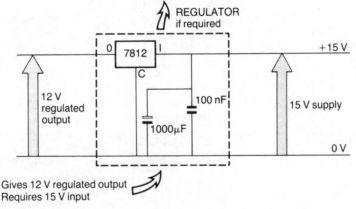

Figure 11.8

If you do not have a smoothed 15 V supply, build in the optional 'regulator' section. Stepper motors require a smooth voltage supply of about 15 V. Batteries could be used as the voltage supply but the motor coils draw a continuous current. You will notice that the motor becomes warm when running, showing that quite a lot of energy is involved. Batteries will run down quickly if used in this way. So a low tension supply is better, but it must be 'smoothed' or regulated when used with a stepper motor. To do this you need to use a voltage regulator chip, as shown in fig 11.8 and 11.9.

The circuit could be built on breadboard but it is more reliable to build a permanent one.

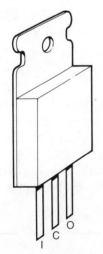

7812 Voltage regulator

Figure 11.9

Activity 11.1

Details of stripboard construction for the stepper motor control chip. You need:

• stripboard 2.5 mm	(RS 433–826)
• 2 SAA1027 driver chips	(RS 300–237)
• 1 7406 Hex inverter	(RS 306–320)
• 1 100 R resistor	(RS 131–132)
• 4 4K7 resistors	(RS 131–334)
• 1 0.1 uF capacitor	(RS 124–178)
• 1 180 R resistor (1W)	(RS 133–661)
• 1 DIL socket 14 pin for 7406 chip	(RS 401–649)
• 2 DIL socket 16 pins for SAA 1027 chips	(RS 401-655)
• regulator (optional)	
• 1 7812 (12 V regulator)	(RS 305–894)
• 1 100 nF capacitor	(RS 124–178)
• 1 1 uF tantalum capacitor	(RS 101–771)
• 1 1000 uF capacitor	(RS 103–610)
• 1 heatsink for regulator	(RS 402–360)

A possible stripboard layout for controlling two motors is shown in fig 11.10. Note that the breaks in the copper strips are marked **x** in the figure.

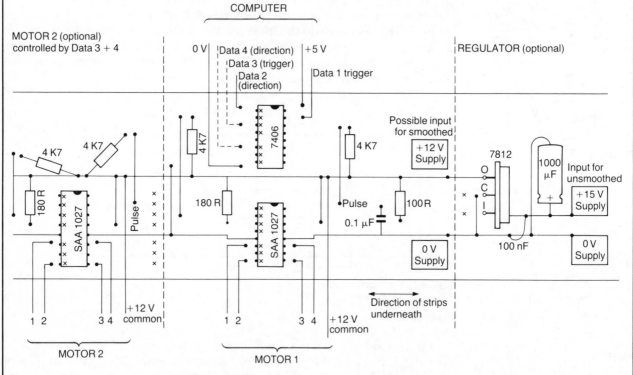

Figure 11.10

Remember that the voltage regulator section is optional. It is needed if your voltage supply is not smoothed. The low tension supply may be smoothed internally, or you could use a battery.

Motor connections and supply voltage

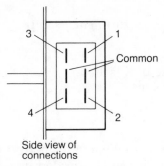

Side view of connections

Figure 11.11

A four coil stepper motor needs five connections, one for each of the coils and a common line. Since the sequence of energising the coils is always the same and repeated, each step is called a 'phase'. You need one further piece of essential information. This is the sequence for connecting the coils – like the example in fig 11.11. There are 24 ways of arranging four wires and, if you do not know the order, you can spend many frustrating hours trying to find it out! Refer to the instructions supplied with your stepper motor and keep them carefully!

Running a stepper motor

The two activities which follow give details for running a stepper motor. Two methods are described. The first uses the computer to arrange the coil sequence. The second uses an SAA 1027 chip as part of a stepper motor control board.

Activity 11.2

Optional, direct computer control of each coil (Method 1).
The aim of this activity is to see how stepper motor coils can be directly controlled by the computer. Do this if you want to find out more about how a stepper motor works or if you don't have a control chip board. Otherwise use method 2, described in activity 11.3.
You need:
- stepper motor (12 V)
- 12/15 V smoothed supply
- user port buffer (Marjon)
- Darlington chip
- breadboard or connecting system for chip. If you kept the breadboard you made in breadboard Activity 3.3 you could use it here. If you have not got this you will need to make one now.
- connecting wires
- (The Chelt-out buffer board incorporates a Darlington chip and can be used to control the coils directly)

Use four data lines from the computer to control octal Darlington drivers in a chip as shown in fig 11.12. Note that the common connection to the coils is linked to the positive voltage supply. You will need to write a computer program to make the Darlingtons activate each phase in turn. The major problem is how to get the sequence right. I suggest that you start by connecting bits (computer control lines) 1, 2, 4, 8 to phase coils 1, 3, 2, 4, as in the figure.

Figure 11.12

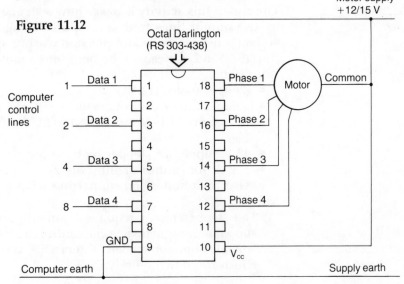

Activity 11.2 continued

If you want to use this system for a practical application it is advisable to spread the heating in the chip. This can be done by sharing the current for each coil between two Darlingtons. Link pins 1 and 2, 17 and 18, 3 and 4, 15 and 16, etc.

Connect the system up and activate each phase in turn. This example program switches bit data 1, 2, 4, 8 in turn:

```
10 ?65122 = 15          Data Direction Register)
20 X = 1                (Makes first value of X = 1)
30 ?65120 = X           (Activates phase coils
40 I = INKEY(10)        (Delay 10/100s)
50 LET X = X*2          (Selects new output value)
60 IF X > 8 THEN X = 1
70 GOTO 30              (Sequence repeats for continuous rotation)
```

Programs written in BASIC are slow. Programs can be speeded up by writing in assembler language. However, BASIC is quite fast enough to cope with the mechanical response of the motor.

Some further investigations

1 Does it improve performance if you energise the coils in pairs?
   i.e. 1 and 2, 2 and 3, 3 and 4, 4 and 1, etc.
   (The SAA 1027) control chip does this)
   A program might give this sequence as follows:
   ```
   ?65120 = 3   data lines 1 & 2 active
   ?65120 = 6   data lines 2 & 3 active
   ?65120 = 12  data lines 3 & 4 active
   ```
   • Can you complete the sequence and make it work?
2 It is claimed that motors can be turned in half steps by activating the coils as follows:
   1 and 2, 2 and 3, 3 and 4, 4 and 1, 1, etc.
   • Is it true?
3 Can you run the motor backwards?

If you are not going to use method 2 in Activity 11.3, there are some further practical problems to try on page 176.

Activity 11.3
Controlling a stepper
motor using a control
chip, (Method 2)

The aim of this activity is to see how a stepper motor can be controlled by two output lines from a computer using the SAA 1027 chip. This system is recommended for practical use of a stepper motor. The control chip (SAA 1027), needs to be built into a motor control circuit.
You need:
   • stepper motor (12 V)
   • stepper motor control circuit – with SAA 1027 chip, e.g. as made in Activity 11.1 (Marjon or NESTEC control boards are also available).
   • 15 V supply for stepper motor (note 1)
   • 5 V dc for control circuit (note 2)
   • User port buffer and connecting wires
Notes:
1 The stepper motor requires a smooth supply. Some low tension supplies are regulated. Some control circuits have a built-in regulator. You need one somewhere! Otherwise, you will have to use batteries which run down quickly.

Activity 11.3 continued

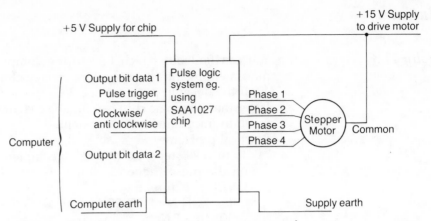

Figure 11.13

2 You may be able to obtain the 5 V from the user port of the computer. The circuit diagram is given in fig 11.13.

Connecting up:
1 Connect your stepper motor to the motor control unit. There are 4 connections for the motor coils and one 'common' line. You will need to find the phase numbers from the details supplied with your motor.
2 Connect the supply voltages (+5 V for the logic chip and +15 V for the motor). MAKE SURE THE POLARITY IS RIGHT.
  Try to test the circuit before connecting it to the computer. Do this by taking the pulse line first to +5 V and then to 0 V. This will not work too well. The chip needs precise voltage changes and simple mechanical connections give too much 'switch bounce'.
3 Connect the data lines to the computer buffer board as follows:
    an earth (ground) connection acting as a reference level
    Pulse signal to data line 1 (control bit 2)
    Forward/reverse to data line 2 (control bit 1)
    +5 V supply to run the chip
  Be prepared to disconnect rapidly if you have any marked reaction on the computer screen!
  • Can you make the motor turn?
You need to write a program that will give 'pulses' by changing output bit 1. A pulse is a swing of voltage from high to low and then high again. The motor will move one step – using the energy from the 15 V supply. The motor will move on one of the transitions – high → low or low → high. It is best to find out which by trial and error. Mostly it will not matter.
The SAA 1027 chip takes a short time to organise the logic. You may find that the computer instructions change too quickly so that you need to introduce a delay between commands.

Suggested starting program:
    10 ?65122=15   Data Direction Register for Marjon board)
    20 ?65120=0
    30 I = INKEY(10)   (Delay 10/100ths sec)
    40 ?65120=1   (Line 1 active)
    50 GOTO 20
  • What happens if you delete the delay?
  • Can you find out whether movement takes place at program line 20 or line 40?
  • Can you reverse the motor?
Line 2 must remain activated. So, the values in the user port address should change between 2 and 3.

Solutions

Activity 11.3

You can find out which line in the computer program causes the step movement by introducing a long delay before line 20 and then before line 40. If the delay in program line 30 is deleted, the program is likely to run faster than the logic chip can organise changes in the field coils. This will result in uncertain step movement.

Practical problems

1 To turn 20 steps, go through a complete sequence of voltage changes on the pulse trigger 20 times. Use a FOR . . . NEXT or REPEAT . . . UNTIL structure, e.g.

```
15  FOR N=1 TO 20
50  NEXT N
```

2 To give 20 steps in the reverse direction, change the voltage on the motor reverse line (bit 2)

```
20  ?65120=2
40  ?65120=3
```

3 Motor speed depends on how quickly you go through the trigger cycle. This is controlled by program line 30, e.g.

```
30  I = INKEY(10)   is fast
30  I = INKEY(100) is slow
```

4 The number of steps to turn 360° (e.g. 48) depends on the structure of the motor. You will need to discover this by trial and error.

Practical problems

When you have the motor working, can you make the motor do the following?

1 Move forward 20 steps
2 Move 20 steps in the reverse direction
3 Move quickly and slowly
4 Turn through 360° and stop
5 Move through a sequence of events which you decide.

Summary

Stepper motors turn in small steps and give precise control of position.
They are significantly more expensive than ordinary motors.
They usually have 4 field coils which have to be activated in the correct phase sequence.
It is essential to have the information about the coil connections for a particular motor.
The phase sequence can be controlled from a computer using four output lines. However, it is more usual to do this with a special chip (SAA 1027).
Then, only two bits of control data are needed from the computer:

pulse trigger
motor direction (forward/reverse)

For practical applications, it is advisable to make up a permanent circuit for using the control chip.

12 Control Projects: Some Suggestions

Introduction

This chapter gives some suggestions for substantial projects where mechanisms, electronics and microcomputer control are brought together. Each involves designing and building. Each includes some form of feedback.

They do require time – something like 20 hours. You also need to be able to leave the equipment set up. There are many reasons why you may wish to tackle projects like these. The best would be – 'because you want to'. Successful solution should give you a great deal of satisfaction.

Organising a project

There are two cardinal rules for organising any project.

The first of these rules is **Don't be over ambitious**. Choose something which looks possible in the time you have available. Practical activities **always** take much longer than you expect, especially when you come across something which does not work properly.

The second rule is that you should break the project into small sections which can be worked on separately. Then, bring the parts together. You can do this with parts of a computer program as well as with the putting together of mechanical and electrical components. Check that each part works as you build it into the system. Whenever possible, make the sections of a program independent of each other. Procedure calls or GOSUB routines help in subdividing computer programs. As you achieve success, you can look for further developments which can be added to the project.

Approaching your project

The first step is to decide what you want to do. Your decision will be based on the answers to a number of questions. For example:

- What equipment is available?
- Is money available to buy any additional items required – will these arrive in time?
- Can the project be completed in the time available?,
- Are you reasonably confident the ideas will work?,
- Can you get advice if you need it?

Work with others if you can. The sharing of ideas and skills is invaluable.

The problem solving process

First you have to define the problem you want to solve and then you can decide on your project brief. You should try to seek out a **number** of possible solutions. You will then be in a position to select the best solution for the time and equipment you have available.

People often talk about a 'problem solving cycle'. I suppose it really means 'keep going' until you find an acceptable solution. Fig 12.1 shows the stages which can be involved in the solving of a project. (If your project is part of an award bearing course, check out carefully what you need to write up. An account of the development stages is often required, together with a discussion of alternative solutions, as well as the equipment and methods you used and the results you found).

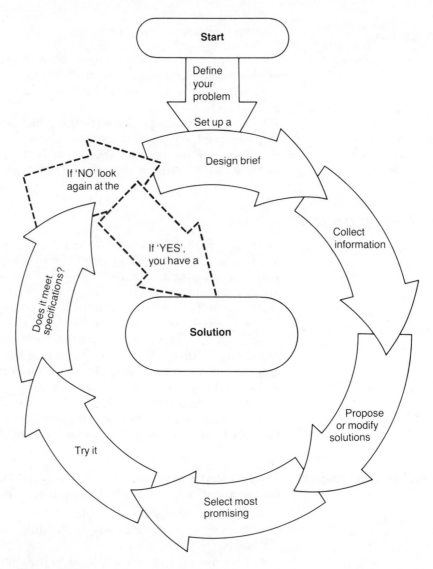

Figure 12.1

Choosing the 'best' solutions: 'doing a PMI'

Most problems have a variety of solutions and you need to select the best.

Decision making can be helped by doing a 'PMI' on each solution. This means listing the **Plus** (P) points, the **Minus** (M) points and the **Interesting** (I) ones. The method helps you to be wide ranging in your thinking. For example, suppose you are trying to decide whether to use ordinary electric motors or stepper motors in a buggy which is to follow a white line. A

'PMI might look like this:

PLUS (P)	MINUS (M)	INTERESTING (I)
Ordinary electric motors		
cheap	don't always start reliably	if feedback is used, position errors can be easily corrected. speed controlled by varying supply voltage or by rapid on/off switching
stepper motors		
very precise position control	expensive	could measure distance travelled by pulse count
	need special pulsing unit	speed controlled by pulse rate

This shows that ordinary motors would do the job quite adequately if sensors are used to provide feedback.

Project suggestions

The possibilities for projects are limitless . . if only you can think of them!

The examples discussed below are intended to show some of what can be done. The first few are discussed in detail and the others more briefly. In each case I have tried to present a number of possible solutions. It is for you to decide which might be the best one.

Outline of discussion

The projects are discussed under the headings of mechanisms, electronics and computer programming. Each of these items is important.

Some thoughts and suggestions on each project are offered. Then some notes on a particular solution are given. Finally, there may be some pointers to further developments you can do. **Don't expect to find precise details. It is up to you to develop your own solutions**.

Design and build . . .

1 a lift which will operate between four floors
2 a conveyor belt which will separate different coloured Lego bricks
3 a buggy which will move around a track drawn on the floor
4 a system that will measure the length and breadth of a house brick
5 a model washing machine
6 a system which will locate a bright light
7 a model train set which operates under computer control; controlling, for example, start/stop, speed, points change, picking up and setting down of trucks
8 a buggy which is controlled by voice commands
9 a system to separate different coloured balls
10 a model warehouse
11 an environmental control system for a greenhouse
12 a system which will maintain a pond at a specified pH
13 a system which will accelerate a large load and change the gearing, depending on the speed of the load
14 a system (full scale or model) which will control natural light – curtains or venetian blinds – and artificial light to maintain a steady lighting level in a room
15 an automatic system to open and close a door (sliding or otherwise)
16 an automatic drinks dispenser
Finally as an example of indulgence . . .
17 a bird feeding system which will only allow small birds to feed

Lift system

Problem –

Build a lift which will operate between four floors

Mechanisms

You will need some kind of shaft to guide the lift. If the cable supporting the lift passes over the spindle of an electric motor, you have the basis for moving the lift.

- Will you use a counter weight to balance the weight of the lift?
- How will you get the lift to run at the right speed?
- Will you use gears or change the motor supply voltage?
- What might happen if the lift overshoots the top or bottom of the shaft?

Electronics

Sensors

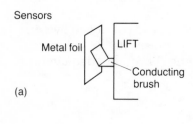

Metal foil

(a)

- How will you reverse the electric motor – by using solid state switches or relays?
- What kind of sensors will you use to test when the lift has reached its floor?

There are a number of possible solutions, some are illustrated in fig 12.2. In the shaft at each floor there could be:

a) a conducting brush which wipes a metal surface, such as aluminium foil

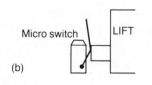

Micro switch

(b)

b) a miniature (micro) switch
c) a magnetic reed switch
d) a light sensitive switch (phototransistor/ldr). Will you need to adjust the light sensitivity?

Instead of having a sensor at each floor, could you measure the number of turns made by the motor? The lift level is directly related to this.

Computer programming

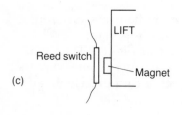

Reed switch

(c)

Assume that you have 4 inputs each linked with a floor. Call the floors 1, 2, 3 and 4. This makes the numbers easy to handle. (If you insist, however, have a '0' or 'ground' floor.) Each floor is linked to a bit in the user address as follows –

floor	bit number
1	1
2	2
3	4
4	8

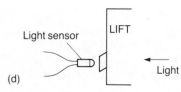

Light sensor

(d)

Figure 12.2

(The Marjon buffer board uses larger numbers on the input lines. You can produce them by multiplying the above by 16.)

You will need to write a program which asks the user which floor he/she wishes to go to. The position of the lift is reported through the input lines. Having decided whether the lift should go up or down, you will need to switch the motor on. You will have to keep looking at the input lines until the required floor is reached, then switch the motor off. Here is a place where the logical AND comes into its own. You could use it to test whether the required floor has been reached. It lets you separate out a particular bit number and test its setting. For example, suppose you want to stop the lift when bit 16 is high. In BASIC, use

```
IF (?65120 AND 16) = 16 THEN LET ?65120 = 0
```

It will work no matter what settings you have on the other lines. If you do not want to use the AND operation, you simply need to keep track of the other numbers in the user port register and act accordingly.

- Can you cope if the lift starts between floors?

Notes on a particular solution

Fig 12.3 shows a complete lift system operating between four floors. The details of how this works is discussed below.

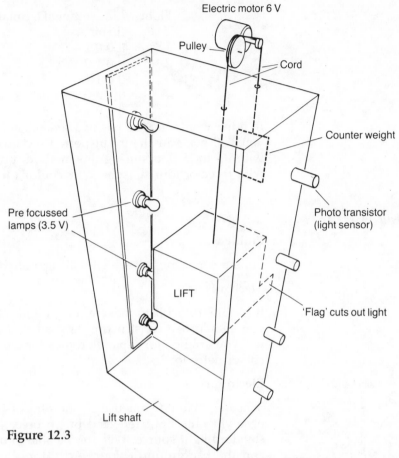

Figure 12.3

1 Phototransistors (RS 806–803) were used as the sensors, one at each floor. These were connected directly to the input lines and illuminated by 3.5 V pre-focussed lamps. The sensitivity was adjusted by changing the light level but a high level was needed and the lamps were run at a higher voltage than specified. Problem – lamps blow easily .

2 When the lift reached a floor the 'flag' carried by the lift cut out the light to a sensor. The 'flag' was needed to give a precise position for activating the sensor. Otherwise the lift stopped at different places when going up and down.

3 The lift tended to over-shoot the floor. This was corrected by putting the motor into reverse for a short time as soon as the required floor was reached. This stopped the lift abruptly. (Goodness knows what this would do to real passengers!)

4 Outline of the program logic was as follows:
   - Ask for required floor
   - Take in sensor data
   - If required floor is same as present floor then react accordingly
   - If required floor < present floor then select motor down
   - If required floor > present floor then select motor up
   - Switch motor on
   - Keep looking at the sensor data until it agrees with the setting for the required floor. When this happens reverse the motor for a short time and then stop.

5 Over-run at the top and bottom of the shaft was not a problem. Friction on the drive shaft was reduced when the lift or counter-weight hit floor and the cord slipped.

6 Could the lift carry the light with it? Being closer to the sensors it would not need to be so bright, so the lamp could be smaller.

Variations, more floors

But what if you have more than 4 floors and only four input lines? You could combine input signals so that more than one line is linked with each floor.

Floor	Line settings (in binary)	Decimal equivalent
1	0 0 0 1	1
2	0 0 1 0	2
3	0 0 1 1	3
4	0 1 0 0	4
5	0 1 0 1	5

In other words, floor 3 has two sensors linked with it. When both are 'on' you will get 3 in the input port. I reckon it should be possible to cope with up to 15 floors using this method, providing some are floors linked with three or four sensors. Why couldn't it cope with 16 floors?

A conveyor belt

Problem

Build a conveyor belt which will separate different coloured Lego blocks

Mechanisms

It is quite difficult to make a robust and reliable conveyor belt. I suggest you should use construction kits such as Fischer-Technik or Lego. How will you arrange for separate routes for the different coloured blocks after colour detection?

Electronics

Sensors – Would you use a phototransistor or ldr to detect colour by observing the light reflected by an object? (fig 12.4) It is wise to use a standard light source. Will you be able to distinguish between the blocks and the background colour? Activator – a solenoid (miniature coil 12 V RS 347–652) can be used to give a brief kick to push an object off a conveyor belt or switch a trap door (fig 12.5). If you are going to use this method you must remember to include a diode in the circuit to protect against any back emf and a high current controller.

Computer programming

Your main problem will be to make the sensor values reliable. Can you have a separate section of program for making the adjustments needed? You will need to arrange the right time delay between sensing a block and taking action for selection.

Notes on a particular solution

Problem – To separate red, white and blue Lego blocks. A possible solution is shown in fig 12.6.

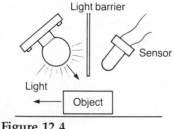

Figure 12.4

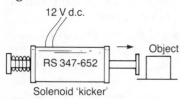

Figure 12.5

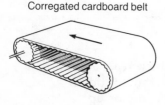

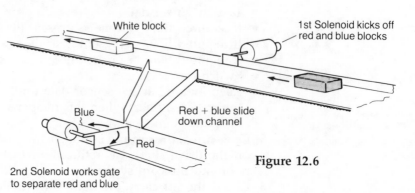

Figure 12.6

1 The blocks were placed on a conveyor belt made of corregated cardboard built into a Fischer-Technik mechanism.
2 The blocks passed through a 'funnel' or centring gates to centre them on the belt.
3 Light from a bright light reflected by each block was monitored by a light sensor. The colour was determined using the analogue input (ADVAL).
4 Red and blue blocks were 'kicked' off the belt (using a solenoid with a paper clip glue-gunned to the end) and then separated by a gate as they slid down a channel (again using a solenoid)

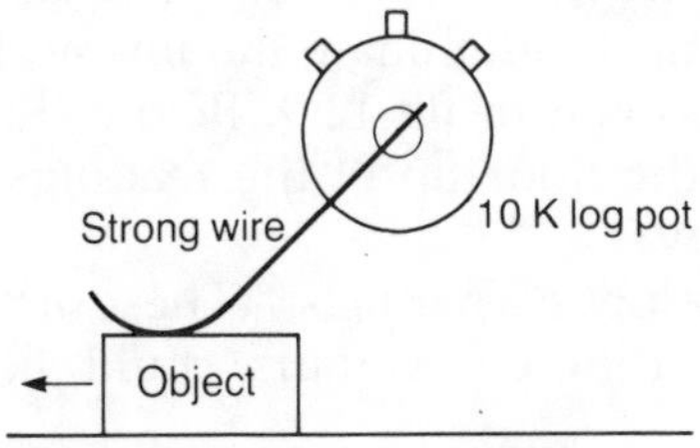

Variations

You could vary the design brief by separating objects of different size or weight. One way of measuring size is to use a variable resistor ('pot') with a lever attached (fig 12.7). Alternatively, your system could be used to select ripe tomatoes from unripe ones. How could you do this?

Figure 12.7

A buggy to follow a track

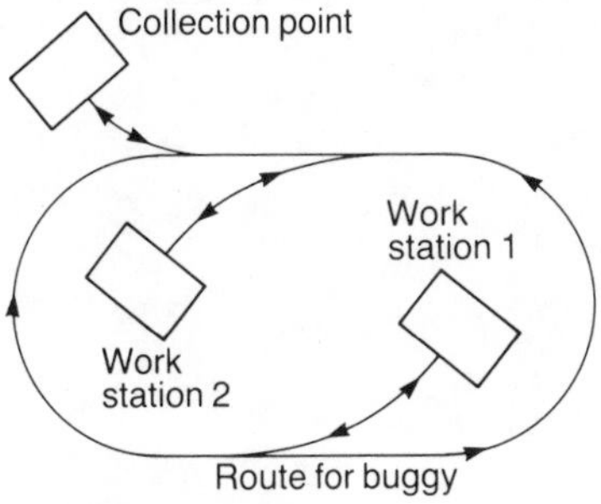

Figure 12.8

Problem

Make a buggy follow a white line simulating a delivery robot in a modern factory
In a factory, parts are collected from one point and delivered to two work stations as shown in fig 12.8. After processing, they are returned to the collection point. In practice, the buggies follow an induction wire laid in the floor.

Mechanisms

There are plenty of problems in this project, so don't try to actually deliver parts! Start off with a ready made buggy. One based on a 'Big Track' motor with two independently controlled drive motors is highly recommended. In following the track, you will have to find the best position for the sensors. Somewhere in front of the buggy is obvious, but, how far out should they be?

Electronics

Suitable sensors are photo-diodes or ldrs as they can distinguish the light reflected from the white line and from the light reflected by the background.
- Will you need to use one, two or three sensors?
- How far from the ground will you place them?
- Will a light source help to give a standard light level?
- What happens if the ambient (natural) light changes?
- Will you arrange for any electronic adjustment in your sensor circuits?
- Will you use the analogue or digital inputs?
See Chapter 8, page 130 for a reliable method worth consideration.

Computer programming

Following a white line
Your logic will be something like:
>   If buggy is on course, move forward.
>   If sensor is off white line, take action to find line.
>   When found, move forward.

Moving into stations
You need to devise some way of reporting when a 'station' has been reached. Your logic then decides whether the buggy goes into the station or not.

Some people find difficulty with the reliability of the sensor readings. I suggest that you arrange to have a separate section in your program to test the sensor values. You can use this to adapt the values for later use in the main part of your program.

Notes on a particular solution

1 A 'Big Track' was used with two drive motors connected to a motor reverse box. This needed four output control lines.
2 Two photo-sensors (ldrs) were fixed onto an extension 15 cm out from the front wheels of the buggy. These sensors tested whether the buggy was on the line. The buggy carried a lamp to illuminate the line and a skirt to cut out any ambient light as shown in fig 12.9. Before the skirt was attached any shadows across the floor upset the readings, and therefore the movement of the buggy.
3 The sensors were connected to the analogue channels. (These are slower acting than digital inputs, but different colours could be detected).
4 A green marker was used on the track to indicate when the buggy had reached a work station (fig 12.10). This gave a different analogue value, which sent the buggy into the work station when appropriate.

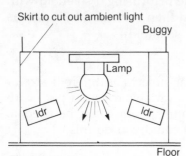

Figure 12.9

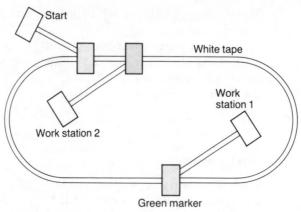

Figure 12.10

5 A microswitch on the front of the buggy reported when a station had been reached.
6 Grandiose schemes of delivering objects to the stations were abandoned as time ran out. Also, more than four output lines would have been needed.

Variations

You can easily develop variations, e.g.
   Follow a black line.
   Make a buggy follow a line of one colour and then switch to a different colour.
   Use a buggy to find the distance between coloured cards on the floor.

A system to measure the size of a house brick

Problem

Build a system which will measure the length and breadth of a house brick.

Mechanisms

One solution is to move a sensor which reports when it touches the brick. Another is to move the brick and use a sensor to report when the ends of the brick arrive.

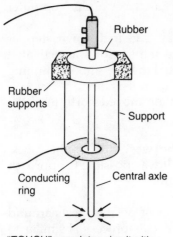

"TOUCH" completes circuit with
conducting ring

Figure 12.11

Electronics

You could use a simple switch contact as a sensor but this only works from one direction.

- Could you build a sensor which indicates when contact is made from any direction? (See fig 12.11).
- Could you use light sensors?

You will need a way of measuring the distance moved. Stepper motors linked through gears or pulleys are well suited for this as they can be used by keeping count of the steps of the motor. However, they are expensive. As an alternative you can use ordinary motors and a sensor to count the revolutions of a wheel as shown in fig 12.12.

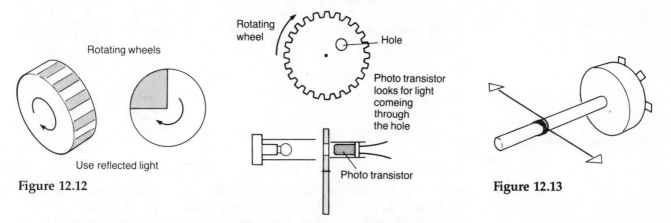

Figure 12.12

Figure 12.13

Another but less accurate method is to use a cord wrapped around a multi-turn potentiometer (fig 12.13).

Computer programming

There are no special problems. You need to be able to control movement in two dimensions and measure position when indicated by the sensor.

Notes on a particular solution

1 A sensor which was sensitive to horizontal contact was supported in a gantry. The structure was made from a mixture of Meccano, Fischer-Technik and junk (fig 12.14).

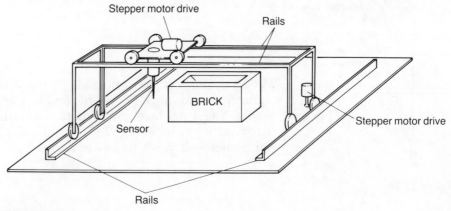

Figure 12.14

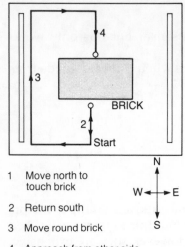

1 Move north to touch brick

2 Return south

3 Move round brick

4 Approach from other side

Figure 12.15

2 The gantry could move North/South and East/West under computer control.

3 N/S and E/W movement was controlled by a geared down stepper motor. The number of steps moved before the sensor was activated was used to measure position. It was essential to have smooth running and located movement, so the wheels ran on rails.

4 The gantry started south of the brick and then moved north until the sensor reported contact (fig 12.15).
The position was recorded.
The sensor backed off, moved around the west side of the block, travelled north and east again. In this way, it was possible to approach the brick from the north and find its breadth.

5 Width was found in a similar way.

6 It was eventually possible to make a number of position tests around the brick and draw its shape on the screen. This process is similar to one used in industry to transfer physical shapes into computer co-ordinates.

7 Changing the height setting of the sensor would allow different 'contour' of a shape to be found.

Variations

The basic mechanism is very similar to a plotter. Replace the sensor with a pen and you have one!

A washing machine

Problem

Build a model washing machine that will fill with water, agitate the dirty washing and, at the end of the washing cycle, empty the water
(Let's leave the spin dry to another time and use an economic cold wash!)

Mechanisms

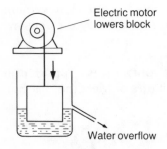

Electric motor lowers block

Water overflow

Moving liquids around can be fun and messy. Mixing water and electricity spells **danger**. So, don't let mains voltage come anywhere near water. Take care to avoid spillage.

You can use gravity to make water flow as shown in fig 12.16. Car windscreen washer pumps (12 V) will move water around – rather slowly, but be patient! Use a 12 V system isolated from the mains supply. Car scrap yards sell pumps quite cheaply. (Immersion petrol pumps also exist – faster acting and useful if you can get hold of them cheaply.)

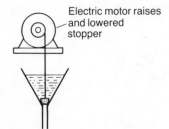

Electric motor raises and lowered stopper

Electronics

A 12 V pump can be controlled with a relay or solid state switch. The agitator should move backwards and forwards so you need to reverse the motor. The water level can be detected using a float linked to a switch or two conductor probes (fig 12.17). Water making contact between the conductor probes switches a transistor circuit.

Figure 12.16

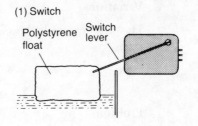

(1) Switch

Polystyrene float

Switch lever

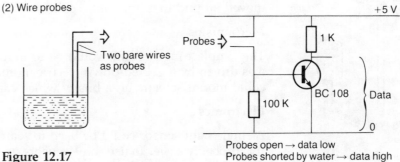

(2) Wire probes

Two bare wires as probes

Probes

+5 V

1 K

BC 108

Data

100 K

0

Probes open → data low
Probes shorted by water → data high

Figure 12.17

Computer programming

A program to control a washing cycle might be:
Fill tank with water.
When full, stop filling.
Begin washing cycle: agitate for set time, then reverse. Repeat this for washing period.
Empty tank.
When empty, stop emptying.

Notes on a particular solution

1 An ice cream container was used with two car windscreen washer pumps to fill and empty it, see fig 12.18.

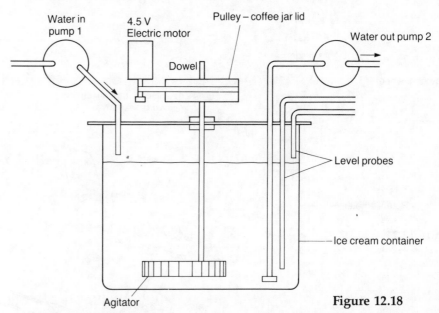

Water in pump 1

4.5 V
Electric motor

Pulley – coffee jar lid

Water out pump 2

Dowel

Level probes

Ice cream container

Agitator

Figure 12.18

2 The agitator was fixed excentrically to wood dowelling and driven from a small electric motor using an elastic band around a pulley wheel (made from a coffee jar lid).
3 Water level was first monitored using a float connected to a switch. This was abandoned when the float got mixed up with the washing! Two sets of wire probes were used to indicate when the machine was full and empty.
4 A single pump could have been used by reversing the water flow.

Variations

The system could be extended to deliver washing powder when appropriate.

A light tracker

Figure 12.19

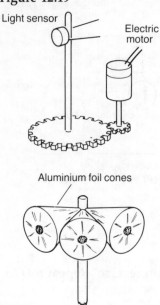

Aluminium foil cones

Figure 12.20

Problem

Build a system which will locate and track a bright light. The light can be moved around in a horizontal plane.

Mechanisms

The simplest mechanism would be to mount a light sensor on a vertical axis driven by a geared-down electric motor (fig 12.19). Alternatively, you could mount sensors on a buggy which can turn on a spot.

Electronics

A single light sensor could be used to search for and locate a bright light. It is probably easier to use three sensors, moving them to keep the middle one in the position of maximum brightness (fig 12.20).
- Will you use analogue or digital inputs?
- Will you use variable resistors to adjust the light sensitivity?

Computer programming

With a single sensor you can do a scan and sample the light levels as you go. Store the readings, return to the start and then move to the position corresponding to the brightest reading. You can base the position on turning time.

Perhaps it is a good time to use an array for storing data? See how to use the DIM statement in BASIC. Counting the steps of a stepper motor would be a much more precise position indicator.
- Could you mount the sensors on the spindle of a potentiometer to give position (fig 12.21)?

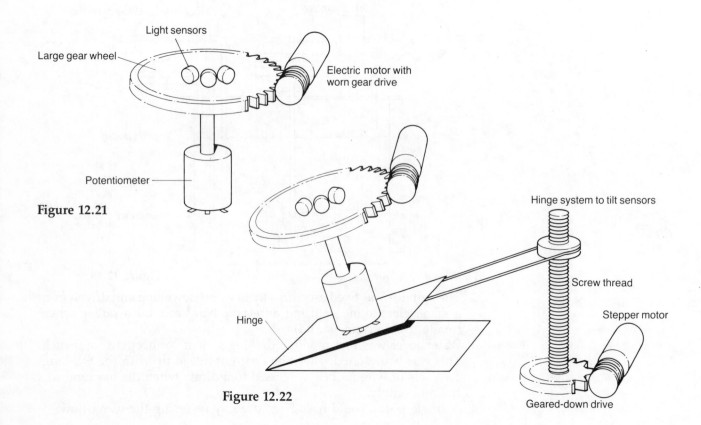

Figure 12.21

Figure 12.22

Notes on a particular solution

1 This started as project for tracking the sun. (There was an idea that the readings could be used to set the orientation of a solar collector.) Three ldrs were fixed onto a Fischer-Technik gear wheel connected to a potentiometer spindle as shown in fig 12.22.
2 The potentiometer was connected to the analogue port and gave the rotational position of the sensors.
3 As the sensors needed to 'look' upward as well as from side to side, the system was mounted on a 'hinge'. This was jacked upward in stages by a few turns of the supporting screw thread.
4 The ldrs were connected to the analogue input.
5 In the development stage, the readings from one of the sensors were displayed on the screen. It was then decided to use a graphics mode to draw out a line showing the brightness level by colours. (Clearly there was some considerable programming expertise at hand!)
6 A program was written to draw a series of lines across the screen as the sensor moved up in steps. Then, a remarkable thing happened. The image which emerged was a kind of primitive TV picture, fig 12.23. So, that was it! The project was diverted to perfecting the 'camera'.

Variations

It is possible to make a light seeking buggy. The buggy scans round to locate maximum brightness. It then turns and moves towards it, see fig 12.24.

Finding and snuffing out a candle has always proved challenging.

A fire engine which squirted water from a balloon was a great success, though it never got round to finding the candle, fig 12.25.

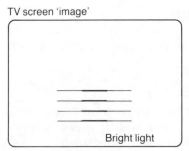

TV screen 'image'

Bright light

White – bright
Yellow – fairly
Red – dim
Black – dark

Figure 12.23

Figure 12.24

Figure 12.25

Using a train set

Problem

Link a model train set with computer control

The variety of things you can do with a train set is almost endless. Most of the mechanical problems have already been solved. This still leaves plenty of electronics and programming problems! Some examples are:

- Can you make the train stop in a station?
- Can you identify carriages or trucks?
- Can you use points to control the routing?
- Can you alter the speed of the train?
- Can you make it accelerate and decelerate?

When you get more advanced you can couple up/decouple carriages and trucks.

Mechanisms

Any model train enthusiast will say that you have to keep the track clean for reliable operation. (Rub with fine emery paper and de-grease with a cloth soaked in meths. Give the drive wheels the same treatment.)

If you use very small gauge (N gauge) you can contain the layout in a small space. However, I have found it difficult to make the track work reliably.

In spite of the space it takes up, I recommend OO gauge, with nickel-silver track. You will probably have to use whatever is readily available.

Electronics

You will want to reverse the train. The 'solid state' motor reverse box will let you do this and also change the speed by fast on/off switching. It's also possible to use a reed relay chip for fast on/off switching but it will have a limited life.

- Which of the many different kinds of sensor will you use to detect train position, e.g. light sensor, magnetic switch, simple lever switch?

Points and decouplers pose special problems., They have coils (solenoids) which need short bursts of quite high current. This moves an iron core in one direction. To reverse the movement, you usually need a second coil. This requires two control data lines. (Could you get away with only one by using a spring mechanism/elastic band for the return?)

You can control a high current using Darlingtons in a chip and linking them in parallel but take great care to switch them off quickly. In practice, this places severe demands on your programming skills and is likely to burn out the Darlingtons fairly quickly.

It is probably better to use a high current transistor or relay – see Chapter 3. **Don't forget the diodes!** (If the low voltage power supply is of limited power, you can store energy in a large capacitor. This can be discharged through the coil giving a large current for a short time.)

You will quickly find the need more than four input and four output lines. The Chelt boards are useful here.

Computer programming

Build up your program in stages which can, as far as possible, be kept separate.

- Could you use procedure calls?

Speed can be controlled by rapidly switching the current on and off. The on/off time is called the mark/space ratio. (Do not use relays – they cannot move quickly enough.)

You accelerate by changing the mark/space ratio. In BASIC, if you want the computer to respond to an input during the acceleration, you will need to interrupt the sequence of instructions with something like

IF ?65120=240 THEN GOTO 3000

At line 3000 you must set the 'logic' right. For example,
if you have interrupted a FOR N=1 TO 1000 . . . NEXT loop, you should complete the loop by setting N=1000.
If you have interrupted a REPEAT . . . UNTIL N=3000 loop, then complete the loop by setting N=3000.
If you do not do this, you will build up a 'nest' of uncompleted loops. The computer will be able to cope with 24 of them and then stop.

Notes on particular solutions

Stopping a train in the station

This was a demonstration for a school fair. It had a single loop of track (fig 12.26). The train always started at light sensor C. The challenge was to have the train stop in the station. People were asked to select the top speed and the running time. On starting, the train accelerated to its top speed, stayed at this speed for the time set and then slowed down and stopped.

Sensors A and B could test whether the train was properly at the station. If both were covered, the train was in the station. If only one was covered, the train was partly in the station. Otherwise, it was out of the station. The situation was reported by the computer.

The set-up used one output line to a solid state switch for controlling the train and three digital input lines for the light sensors.

A more complex layout

This was built up by a number of groups in succession. The computer interfacing used eight printer port lines as outputs, eight user port lines and four analogue channels as inputs.

The track had two loops and a spur as shown, fig 12.27.

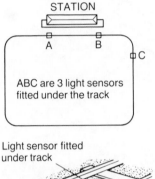

ABC are 3 light sensors fitted under the track

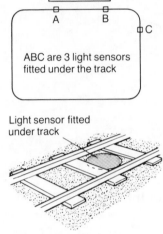

Light sensor fitted under track

Figure 12.26

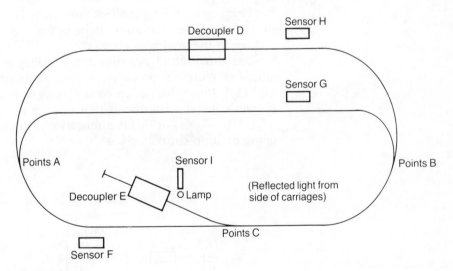

Figure 12.27

The circuit connections were fixed to the board and **labelled**. In this way, succeeding people working with the set were able to build upon the work of others.

We had visions of writing a program to rearrange a set of trucks . . . but have never quite got far enough.

A vehicle controlled by voice commands

Problem

Make a buggy move forward, stop, turn left and right in response to voice commands.

This is open loop control – there is no feedback to report the position of the buggy. Unless you consider the operator as part of the system, then s/he provides a feedback loop! (fig 12.28).

Figure 12.28

Mechanisms

You need two motors to control the movement of the buggy.

Electronics

You have to detect the voice command and arrange for the computer to interpret its meaning. Detections looks fairly easy. You need a microphone and an amplifier. The signal can be fed into the analogue port for analysis.

There is a major problem, however. The analogue port measures up to 1.8 V with a maximum voltage of 5 V. So, you need to supply the right voltage to the analogue channel.

You must avoid negative input voltages. I suggest that you use an amplifier with 5 V (max) dc supply without a negative supply. Having said that, I have spent some frustrating hours trying to make an amplifier system work. I recommend that you try the circuit in fig 12.29. It's taken from 'The Book', an MEP publication. It helps if you have experience of using op amp chips like the 741.

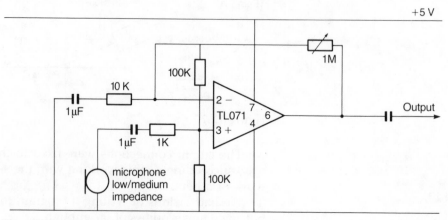

Figure 12.29

Try four commands – forward, turn left, turn right, stop. You must decide how to match the signal with one of the commands.

Computer programming

On saying a command, you can store a set of readings from the analogue port. It's easy to get a graph showing how the sound level changes with time (See Chapter 8 page 127).

You should find a different pattern for each command, as shown in fig 12.30.

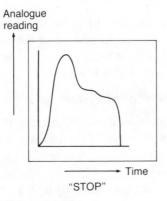 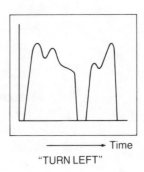

"STOP"   "TURN LEFT"

Figure 12.30

- Can you find a way of matching the pattern with the 'standard' commands?
- Having done this, can you set the output lines to make the buggy respond?

Notes on particular solutions

The speech inputs were displayed graphically.
Three methods were developed to identify the command:
(a) measure the time duration of the command.
(b) find the fraction of time where the signal exceeds a particular level
(c) find the area under the curve.
Each only worked after the speaker had done a great deal of training!

The third needed considerable time for computation. By the time this was completed, the buggy had moved on some distance and crashed!

Variation

Would a whistle work?

Some other projects

The previous project ideas have been discussed in some detail. The remaining examples are treated more briefly.

A system to separate different coloured balls

This is similar to project 2 but is much easier and quicker to build.

If you use a drawing board and table tennis sized balls, channels to contain the balls can easily be made using card and drawing pins. A solenoid can be used to direct coloured balls down a different channel. (See fig 12.31)

A model warehouse

● Can you pick up an object from one place and deposit it at another?
You could develop the project to deliver objects to a variety of places. Organising the mechanisms is going to be a major part of this project. You need to be able to move a 'grabber' up and down and from side to side. The grabber could hold objects using an electromagnet.

Controlling a jaw is rather more complex. See Chapter 9, page 154 for more details.

If you have two motors, one for up/down and the other for left/right you need four control lines. You require some more output lines to control the grabber.

A single data line could control an electromagnet but two will be needed for a 'jaw'. (One to open and the other to close.) This means that you will want to use an output control with more than four lines, e.g. Chelt-out board with eight lines.

An environmental control system for a greenhouse

You could measure: moisture level in ground, temperature and light level.
● Can you devise ways of controlling them?

Heating could be by a high wattage low voltage lamp or possibly by controlling the circulation of hot water. (If you use water, take great care over your safety precautions.) Ventilation can be arranged by opening and closing windows.
● What about an automatic nutrient feed system?

A system which will maintain a pond at a specified pH

You must decide the pH of the water supply.
This was a response to a situation where water was collected from a roof and fed to a pond. The water supplied was always at a pH which was too high. A pH meter can be connected to the analogue port.
● Can you devise a way of keeping the pond pH at the right level?

A system which will accelerate a large load and change gearing depending on the speed of the load

This is really an automatic gear changing system. The idea came from looking at a bus control gear.

A system which will control natural light (using curtains or venetian blinds) and artificial light to maintain a steady lighting level in a room

Perhaps I should admit that I have never seen these last two actually built.

An automatic sliding door

The construction of a model automatic sliding door is quite a challenge to mechanical skills. Once made, it gives opportunity to develop quite a number of sensor and logic ideas. (e.g. how will you stop the door when fully open or closed? How long before the door shuts again? What happens if another person walks into a closing door?)

An automatic drinks dispenser

An automatic drinks dispenser looks like an opportunity to make a mess! (Again, remember the safety precautions when using water.) You could have different drinks available and the system could select the one required. A crude, but nevertheless effective solution is shown in fig 12.31.

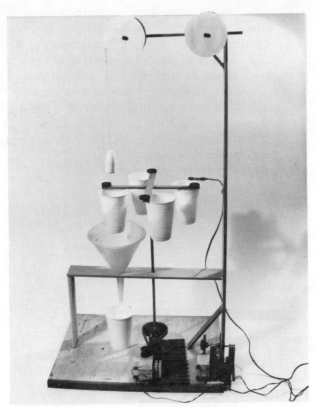

Figure 12.31

Model bird feeder

Finally, something which gave a great deal of fun just before one Christmas. This was a model of a bird feeding system which will allow only small birds to feed. See fig 12.32. A bird alighting on the platform caused it to move down some distance, depending on the weight. This turned a potentiometer allowing the weight to be estimated. Violent treatments for large birds were humanely rejected. If the bird was too heavy, an arm moved round and pushed it aside. The arm itself was pivoted on a potentiometer to give information about its position.

Don't dismiss this as pure nonsense!

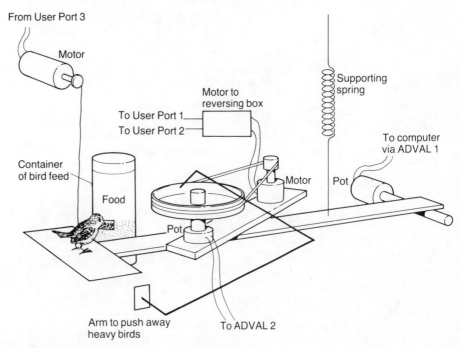

Figure 12.32

It involves some good example of mechanisms, particularly the turning effects of a force. The electronics involved reliable use of two voltage dividers and the computing examples of feedback. Basically it gave a great deal of satisfaction and sense of achievement. This remained undiminished even when a cynic pointed out that it could be done much more simply if a heavy bird simply closed a shutter on the feeder. And indeed this is true. Computer control, however, offers a great deal of flexibility. It would be easy to adjust the size of bird allowed to feed or to count the number of birds feeding each hour. The control principles can be applied in a wide variety of situations.

Happy problem solving!

Appendix

This gives a list of suppliers for the equipment you will need. Some of these suppliers provide general electrical components, others special pieces of equipment only, as indicated.

RS Components
PO Box 99
Corby, Northants NN17 9RS
Tel: (0536) 201201   (01) 360 8600

RS pride themselves on providing a fast, reliable service. They have a very comprehensive list of components. Their catalogue will be found somewhere in most schools and institutions dealing with electronics.

This book uses the RS references for components. RS have a technical information service and supply data leaflets. They do not, however, deal directly with members of the general public.

Farnell Components
Canal Road
Leeds LS12 2TU
Tel: (0532) 636311

This is another firm with a comprehensive list of components. Postage and packing are extra.

Rapid Electronics
Hill Farm Industrial Estate
Boxted, Colchester
Essex CO4 5RD
Tel: 0206 272730

Rapid Electronics supply basic items at competitive prices and aims for fast despatch.

Maplin Supplies
PO Box 3, Rayleigh,
Essex SS6 8LR
Tel: (0702) 554155

Maplin deals directly with the general public and has shops in some cities. Its comprehensive catalogue can be bought at W H Smith. Prices include VAT and usually include postage and packing.

There are other suppliers worth consideration, e.g.

MS Components Ltd
Zephyr House, Waring St
West Norwood
London SE27 9LH
Tel: (01) 670 4466

JPR Electronics
Unit M, Kingsway Industrial Estate
Kingsway, Luton
Beds LU1 1LP
Tel: (0582) 410055

Some items can only be obtained from particular suppliers. These are listed below.

Pcbs for making up into permanent units, Marjon buffer board (pcb), solid state motor reverse board (pcb) and stepper motor board (pcb)

> Physics Department
> College St Mark and John,
> Derriford Rd
> Plymouth, Devon PL6 8BH
> Tel: (0752) 777188

Bigtrack Motor

> Greenweld
> 443 Millbrook Rd
> Southampton SO1 0HX
> Tel: (0703) 772501

DIY buggy kit and stepper motor board (pcb), stepper motor and SAA 1027 chip

> NESTEC
> Kilder House
> Coach Land Campus
> Newcastle upon Tyne NE7 7XA
> Tel: (0632) 663409

4.5 V dc motors. These are not always in stock at a reasonable price. Try your local SATRO centre or:

> PROOPS
> 52 Tottenham Court Rd
> London W1P 0BA
> Tel: (01) 636 4420

> Surplus Buying Agency
> Woodbourne Rd School
> Woodbrown Rd
> Sheffield S9 3LQ
> Tel: (0742) 448647

> Philip Harris
> Lynn Lane, Shenstone
> Litchfield
> Staffs WS14 0EE
> Tel: (0453) 480077

Thermistors, Siemens part K164-2.2 K (25p each)

> Electrovalue
> 28 St Judes Rd
> Englefield Green
> Egham
> Surrey TW20 0HB
> Tel: (0784) 33603

Temperature sensors – Mullard ref. KTY83-100 (30p each), analogue port pcb.

Science Dept
College St Paul and St Mary
The Park,
Cheltenham,
Glos GL52 3JL
Tel: (0242) 513836